QUANTUM PHYSICS
AND
THE PHILOSOPHICAL TRADITION

Quantum Physics
and
The Philosophical
Tradition

BY

AAGE PETERSEN

Published in cooperation with

BELFER GRADUATE SCHOOL OF SCIENCE

YESHIVA UNIVERSITY

NEW YORK

by

THE M.I.T. PRESS

MASSACHUSETTS INSTITUTE OF TECHNOLOGY

CAMBRIDGE, MASSACHUSETTS,

AND LONDON, ENGLAND

Library of Congress Catalog Card Number : 68-17359

MADE AND PRINTED IN GREAT BRITAIN BY
WILLIAM CLOWES AND SONS, LIMITED, LONDON AND BECCLES

To Betty and Troels

Denne afhandling er af det matematisk-naturviden-
skabelige fakultet ved Københavns universitet antaget
til offentligt at forsvares for den filosofiske doktorgrad.

København, den 6. december 1966,

Mogens Pihl
h.a. dec.

PREFACE

Out of the study of the foundations of quantum mechanics there is growing a new view about the nature of physics. Although this view, to which Niels Bohr and Werner Heisenberg especially have contributed, is still only partially developed, the characteristics that have emerged indicate that it has general significance. There have been two principal lines of investigation into its epistemological consequences. One traces logical analogies between the description problems in quantum physics and those in other fields such as biology, psychology, and the social sciences. The other investigates the relation of the new view of physics to some of the concepts and doctrines that form the core of the Western philosophical tradition.

This book tries to pursue the second line of investigation. It is no more than a preliminary treatment and the topic still lacks a clear structure. Yet I hope that the perspective in which it is viewed has made possible a sharper formulation of some of the issues.

Close contact with Niels Bohr in the period 1952–62 greatly influenced my attitude to the topic. I have also profited much from discussions with Peter Zinkernagel and J. Witt-Hansen, University of Copenhagen; Frederick Werner, Xavier University, Cincinnati, Ohio; Paul Forman, University of Rochester, New York; and Yakir Aharonov and Arthur Komar, Belfer Graduate School of Science, Yeshiva University, New York.

Further, my thanks are due to F. O. Schmitt, Massachusetts Institute of Technology, for sponsoring a grant from the American Academy of Arts and Science, and to Victor Butterfield and Paul Horgan for their hospitality at the Center for Advanced Studies, Wesleyan University, Middletown, Conn.

Finally, 1 want to thank Edel Tanggaard, Tania Senff, and Harriet Nachmann for help in typing the manuscript.

AAGE PETERSEN

Belfer Graduate School of Science
Yeshiva University, New York
February, 1967

CONTENTS

CONTENTS

INTRODUCTION

Quantum physics is one of the major scientific advances in this century. It has vastly extended the scope of the mathematical description of nature. This extension has deepened our insight into the foundations of physics. It may also cause profound changes in our philosophical outlook.

The mathematical part of quantum mechanics was developed long ago. Thorough analysis of its foundations has clarified most of its paradoxes and revealed many new and surprising features of physical description. Yet there is not full agreement about its interpretation and the question may be far from closed. Investigation of quantum physics' philosophical significance is still in a formative state.

The bases of the most widely accepted interpretation of the quantal formalism were laid in discussions between Heisenberg and Bohr in Copenhagen in the winter of 1926–27. This interpretation, often called the Copenhagen interpretation, is centered around the relations of indeterminacy and the concept of complementarity. It was thoroughly tested and much refined in the following years, particularly in the famous debate with Einstein, and in Bohr and Rosenfeld's analysis of the measurability of field quantities in 1933. But despite its remarkable success in illuminating paradoxes, and in answering objections against the consistency and completeness of the nonrelativistic quantal description, and even in

[1]

coping with more advanced measuring problems, the Copenhagen interpretation has continued to meet strong opposition from many physicists and philosophers. The controversy has greatly stimulated interest in the topic.

In exploring the broad implications of the quantum issue, two principal directions have been followed. So far, they have been pursued almost completely independently, and no detailed appraisal of their interrelation has yet been made. The first line of investigation, which was pursued intensely by Bohr, is a study of the concept of complementarity. The second, to which especially Heisenberg has contributed, explores quantum physics' relation to the philosophical tradition.

Basic to the study of complementarity is the view that many of the well-known difficulties in philosophy have appeared because philosophers have lacked adequate logical or conceptual tools to represent the fundamental epistemological aspects of our situation. In this respect the condition in philosophy may be compared with familiar cases in physics where an appropriate conceptual frame for describing a particular domain of experience was or is still lacking, for example pre-Newtonian mechanical theories, pre-quantal explanations of the stability of physical objects and the specificity of their properties, or the present state of affairs in elementary particle physics. Further, according to this view, the quantal description has provided us with a logical technique which is well suited for analyzing epistemological problems.

That such a technique could come from quantum physics is due to a profound kinship between the description problems in quantum theory and in philosophy. The quantum description problem stems from the distinction between the physical system that is being investigated and the instruments that specify the experimental conditions under which the system is observed. It is up to the experimenter to place the partition between system and instrument, *i.e.* to delineate the system and to decide which apparatus to use for its investigation. In classical physics, the only aspect of the system–instrument distinction that seemed to require analysis was the relativity problem concerning the connection between observations made on the same system by observers moving relative to each other. In quantum physics, new aspects of the system–instrument relationship came to light.

The finitude of the quantum constant implies that the system's interaction with the instruments cannot be fully defined or controlled. Thus, the system is to some extent inextricably coupled to the instrument used to investigate it, and the description of a quantum phenomenon must include a specification of the whole experimental arrangement. Because of the irreducible and uncontrollable quantum coupling between system and apparatus, different types of instruments, like those necessary to define a state of a system in classical theory, cannot be used concurrently in observing a quantum system. Quantum phenomena which are brought about by use of the same type of object but different types of instruments therefore exhibit a new relationship; they are said to be complementary to each other.

Bohr held that the central feature of human knowledge is our distinction between subject and object, and that the problems engendered by this distinction are logically similar to those which the instrument–system distinction gives rise to in quantum physics and which can be handled by the quantal description and the concept of complementarity. The movability of the partition between subject and object enables us, in some sense, to talk about ourselves. In many situations, for example in introspection, experiences are inseparable from the circumstances under which they occur, and they are thus highly sensitive to the placing of the partition. Statements referring to different placings of the partition are complementary in the sense of quantum physics. The contrasts between complementary experiences are related to the differences in the conditions under which they occur. The richness of man's situation is rooted in the multiplicity of the conditions under which experience appears, or in the variety of ways of placing the object–subject partition.

Bohr investigated a number of analogies between complementary quantum phenomena and complementary phenomena in other fields, such as biology, psychology and the social sciences. He maintained that the logical basis for the existence of organisms is the complementarity between exhaustive physical analysis of a system and the conditions under which it may display features of life. Just as an atom will show chemical properties only when placed under "chemical" conditions, so an organism will display genuinely biological properties only under "biological" conditions. An atom will show a characteristic line spectrum when placed in a spectroscope; when observed in a microscope it will yield information about the location of its nucleus and electrons. Under the conditions set by the microscope, no trace of a chemical spectrum will appear.

Bohr's way of thinking is particularly conspicuous in his discussion of the problem of free will. In his view, the issue is not to determine whether or not our will is free. An expression like "I will" is indispensable in describing psychological experiences, just as the ordinary physical concepts are indispensable in describing physi-

[4]

cal phenomena. The problem is to apply the relevant concepts unambiguously. This must be clarified by investigating the conditions that define the situations to which these concepts refer. Bohr regarded these situations as purely psychological. Introspection shows that when one is totally immersed in pondering motives for an action or reasons for a decision, one does not experience a feeling of volition. Conversely, a situation characterized by an expression like "I will" is incompatible with a situation of deliberation. Thus the psychological situations where one cannot analyze motives provide room for the concept of volition. Such situations, which are analogous to quantum states that possess a definite energy and exclude space–time coordination, form an integral part of psychological experience. Our freedom to act is as "real" as the stationary states of an atom.

Bohr argued that men have always used a complementary mode of description to represent their states of mind. He saw relations of complementarity between instinct and reason, individual and society, compassion and justice. In fact, he considered such relations of complementarity the dominant feature in all fields where describing experience requires considering the conditions under which experience is gained. In physics the measuring apparatus specifies these conditions. In other fields the conditions are less explicitly stated, but it is essential to be aware of them to secure unambiguous description and to avoid paradoxes.

For thirty-five years Bohr struggled to develop the idea of complementarity into a precise and comprehensive philosophical viewpoint. He never wrote an extensive treatise on complementarity. Over the years he published a series of brief essays that summarized the state of his thinking.[1] Here the structure of quantum physics was made a mold for a philosophy of nature and man, an attitude to human life.

* * *

The second direction from which the question of the philosophical significance of the quantal description has been approached is the study of the meeting between quantum physics and the philosophical tradition. The following investigation deals with an important part of this diverse topic—the implications of the quantal description for some of the basic concepts and doctrines of traditional metaphysics and epistemology. At present there is a wide range of views among physicists as well as among philosophers on the topic's content, significance, and proper treatment. A survey of some main contributions may indicate the present state of the discussion. Broadly speaking, the views on the meeting of quantum physics and our philosophical tradition may be divided into five classes.

Quantum mechanics has been thought of as deviating from the proper path of science and violating basic tenets of a rational description of nature. A version of this view was held by Schrödinger, the creator of wave mechanics. On the basis of an interesting investigation of the position of quantum physics in our intellectual tradition[2] he

[1] Most of these essays are included in the three collections *Atomic Theory and the Description of Nature*, Cambridge, 1934 (reprinted 1961); *Atomic Physics and Human Knowledge*, New York, 1958; *Essays 1958–1962 on Atomic Physics and Human Knowledge*, New York, 1963.

[2] "Die Besonderheit des Weltbilds der Naturwissenschaft," *Acta Physica Austria* **1**, 201 (1948). See also *Science and Hu-*

concluded that contemporary discussion of the quantum problem may be compared to the decadent era in late Antiquity when science lost connection with its historical roots and was transformed into mysticism and superstition. He reached this radical conclusion through a logical and historical study of especially Ancient Greek philosophy, in which he tried to identify the peculiarities of our conception of a rational approach to the study of nature. He found that this approach does exhibit definite traits, that these are historically conditioned, and that they do not constitute the only possible form of thought.

The rational approach is based on two characteristic assumptions. The first is that nature is comprehensible, that experience may be ordered, that the world is not bewitched. The second is called the assumption of "objectivability," *i.e.* that the knowing subject plays the role of a detached observer and may be left out of the world picture.

The two assumptions, on which the whole scientific tradition rests, are not independent: comprehensibility is paid for by pushing back the subject. The assumptions are restrictive, and attempts to create a complete world picture out of them lead to logical troubles. Since any such picture has no room for the observing and knowing subject, it must contain "blind spots." Attempts to erase these spots without abandoning the mode of thought defined by the two assumptions have caused many of the well known antinomies and paradoxes in the theory of

---

manism, Cambridge, 1952; *Die Natur und die Griechen*, Hamburg, 1956; "Die gegenwärtige Situation in der Quantenmechanik," *Die Naturwissenschaften* **23**, 807, 823, 841 (1935); "Are there Quantum Jumps?" *The British Journal for the Philosophy of Science* **3**, 109 (1952).

knowledge. A comprehensive conception of nature where the subject has its proper place requires a change of approach. Philosophy must face this necessity, but science, to remain rational, must proceed on the given basis.

In Schrödinger's opinion, the Copenhagen interpretation of quantum mechanics violates both of the axioms underlying an orderly objective world picture. Bohr's view that the quantal formalism is solely a device to produce predictions that are obtained under specified conditions is held to be incompatible with the assumption of comprehensibility. Furthermore, Heisenberg and Bohr's "neo-Machian" interpretation of the indeterminacy relations brings the subject–object relation out of philosophy into the science of inanimate matter. Thus it is impossible to retain objectivity even there. Judged on the background of the intellectual tradition, quantum physics appears to be a deviation or even a step backwards.

Schrödinger's bold and challenging view raises many interesting questions about the nature of the encounter between quantum physics and traditional philosophy. Above all, it suggests that this encounter may touch the very roots of our general outlook. Also it shows some of the difficulties of an investigation that is neither purely historical nor purely logical. Schrödinger's study has not been continued and developed into a detailed argument.

Einstein, another pioneer of quantum physics, shared Schrödinger's conviction that the current interpretation of the quantal formalism is at variance with basic ideas of scientific description. His criticism derived from a philosophical attitude which, though not identical with that of any particular school, was remarkably close to the philosophical tradition.

[8]

The core of Einstein's philosophy[1] is his sharp distinction between "the world of sensory experience" and "the world of concepts and propositions". It is the task of science to orient us in the maze of sense impressions. The concepts are constructed for this purpose. A concept's justification depends exclusively on the help it gives in bringing order among sense impressions.

The sense data are considered given and knowable. Concepts cannot be derived inductively from these data, but are "free creations of the human (or animal) mind." Though there are no fixed rules for coordinating concepts with sense data, rules are as necessary for constructing a system of concepts as they are in playing a game. Yet these rules are not *a priori*, but are created by us, and again success is the only criterion.

The connection between elementary concepts and sense data is open to intuitive understanding only. The connection "is not analogous to that of soup to beef, but rather of wardrobe number to overcoat."[2] Despite the lack of logical dependence "the universe of ideas is just as little independent of the nature of our experiences as clothes are of the form of the human body."[3] Only because there are connections between the sensory and the conceptual world is the scientific system of concepts more than an empty scheme. The connections enable scientific

[1] See "Physics and Reality," *Journal of the Franklin Institute* **221**, 349 (1936) (included in *Out of My Later Years*, New York, 1950); "Quanten-Mechanik und Wirklichkeit," *Dialectica* **2**, 320 (1948); and especially Einstein's "Autobiographical Notes" and his "Remarks to the Essays Appearing in this Collective Volume" in *Albert Einstein: Philosopher-Scientist* (P. A. Schilpp, ed.), Evanston, 1949.

[2] *Out of My Later Years*, p. 64.

[3] *The Meaning of Relativity*, 3rd ed., 1950, p. 2.

theorems to be statements about complexes of sense data.

The concept that most characterizes our way of bringing order into our sense experiences is that of "the real external world." The first step in forming this concept is to construct the notion "bodily object." "Out of the multitude of our sense experiences we take, mentally and arbitrarily, certain repeatedly occurring complexes of sense impressions (partly in conjunction with sense impressions which are interpreted as signs for sense experiences of others), and we attribute to them a meaning— the meaning of the bodily object."[1] The second step is to attach to the concept of bodily object "a significance, which is to a high degree independent of the sense impression which originally gives rise to it. This is what we mean when we attribute to the bodily object 'a real existence.'"[2]

In Einstein's view, the Copenhagen interpretation of quantum physics is unacceptable because it is at variance with the program of physical description based on the concept of a real external world independent of our sense experience. This is strikingly brought out by the so-called Einstein–Podolsky–Rosen paradox[3] that concerns the conclusions to be drawn about a physical system A from measurements made on another system B with which A has previously interacted. If one measures B's position, one can infer the position of A; if B's momentum is measured, the momentum of A can be inferred. It is true that quantum physics prevents us from making both

[1] *Out of My Later Years*, p. 59.

[2] *Out of My Later Years*, p. 60.

[3] A. Einstein, B. Podolsky, N. Rosen, "Can Quantum Mechanical Description of Physical Reality Be Considered Complete?" *Phys. Rev.* **47**, 777 (1935).

of these measurements on B concurrently, but it permits us to make either one, and in neither case do we interact physically with A. Therefore if we assert that the quantum formalism yields a complete description of the situation, then we cannot maintain that A is in a definite physical condition after its interaction with B. Its condition depends on what at this stage we choose to do to B.

As indicated, Einstein did not consider the concept of objective reality to be *a priori*; nor did he claim that this concept is the only possible basis for scientific description. But he knew of no better basis, and he felt that stronger arguments than those adduced by the Copenhagen school were needed in order to give up the program entailed in the category of objective reality. The conviction that physical science will remain a description of the objective reality forces us to consider quantum physics as an incomplete conceptual scheme. It induces us to continue to look for concepts that can give us an "inside view" of what happens to a single physical system in quantum processes.

* * *

A second attitude to the question of quantum physics' relation to traditional philosophy is that physics and philosophy not only are now pursued independently, but are indeed completely autonomous subjects. It is argued that quantum physics contains no philosophical assumptions and has no philosophical implications. At any rate, concepts like physical reality, objectivity, the lawfulness of nature, and the limitations of human knowledge do not seem to occur in any important argument in physical discussion. Apparently such concepts are always peripheral to the interesting problems.

[11]

Central issues in quantum physics seem to be largely insensitive to our view of the meaning of reality. Whether we have a common-sense attitude or some more sophisticated view is immaterial, provided that our conception of reality does not constrain our imagination. Quantum mechanics has not accentuated the significance of ontological concepts, but has removed the last traces of their celestial halo. It has shown more clearly than ever that ontological concepts are not in the focus of physical research. Since their role in physics appears to be trivial, it is difficult to believe that they hold the key to deep philosophical insights. The extraordinary attention they have received from philosophers seems to have been misdirected.

An interesting version of this view, which is widely held among physicists, has been presented by Dancoff.[1] He argued that in physics the word "exist" can be properly used only about the experimental data. Theoretical concepts, like electron and neutrino, employed to correlate such data, cannot meaningfully be said to exist or to not exist in an ontological sense. "Strictly speaking, an electron is merely that thing—that state of affairs— which is defined by the Schrödinger–Dirac theory ... When one asks: 'Does the electron exist'—that is the same as asking: 'Do the data exist? Are the experiments real?'"[2] Many people want to consider an electron "as something more than a convenient grouping of data. They like to think that in some extra-physical sense there 'really is' an electron ... that an electron exists independently of our experiments and theory. It is really,

[1] "Does the Neutrino *Really* Exist?" *Bulletin of the Atomic Scientists* **8**, 139 (1952).
[2] *Op. cit.*, p. 140.

absolutely there. I don't say that such a point of view can be shown to be logically false . . . But I do think that it is a very dangerous and unproductive point of view. It actually hampers the work of physics."[1]

To guard ourselves against shocks like those produced by relativity and quantum theory which made most physicists feel that "they were asked to surrender hallowed and cherished concepts that had become set in granite for them . . . one of the things we must be most careful about is to refrain from attaching absolute reality to concepts like the electron, energy, mass, etc. They are useful, they are expedient, but they are also expendable."[2] The crucial point is that "theorists don't want to be bound in developing new theories by somebody's prejudice about what it is that really exists. If I can find a new theory which is superior to quantum mechanics and which does not mention electrons anywhere, then away with electrons—let's hear no more about them! But the man for whom electrons have become real and unquestionable is forever limited in his conception of possible new theories."[3]

Faced with the fact that the solutions of Schrödinger's equation in some cases are similar to those of classical equations describing particle motion, and in other cases are more like the equations of wave motion, "the believers in the absolute reality of the electron will often say, for example, that the electron really is a particle but it is the perversity of nature which prevents us from making exact measurements on this particle. We see this particle only through a ground glass, darkly. There is a principle, unfortunately called by some the uncertainty

---

[1] *Ibid.*   [2] *Op. cit.*, p. 141.   [3] *Op. cit.*, p. 140.

principle, which is said to express the limitation on measuring the position and velocity of the electron. I prefer to say there is no uncertainty involved anywhere. It is not necessary to assume that there really is a point electron; consequently, there is no position or velocity of anything to be uncertain about. The electron may behave only approximately like a particle, or approximately like a wave. But it always behaves precisely and without any uncertainty, like a solution of Dirac's equation, *i.e.* precisely like an electron.

"The concept of a particle, such as an electron, neutrino, etc. may be considered simply a chapter heading in some book of theoretical calculations. Each chapter covers all the calculations on a certain class of experiments. If the results of the calculations check the experiments, then the theory is good, and the concept may be said to be *suitable*, or *appropriate* . . . As to whether it is something more, something *real* in some sense or other, it doesn't appear possible to define that question in a physically meaningful way."[1] Dancoff presumably found no obscurity or depth in the statement that experimental data exist, and so saw no further points of interest in the concept of physical reality.

* * *

The third attitude to quantum physics' relation to traditional philosophy is that the philosophical features of the situation in quantum physics can be fully encompassed within the framework of traditional metaphysics and epistemology. There have been many attempts to show that quantum physics supports one or another philosophical school. Thus it has been widely held that the

[1] *Op. cit.*, p. 140f.

[14]

Copenhagen interpretation of the quantal description con-
firms the so-called Empirist or Positivist conception of
the problems of reality and knowledge.[1] From another
side it has been argued that quantum physics, correctly
interpreted, conforms with the principles of Dialectical
Materialism.[2] It has also been maintained that the characteristics of the quantum theory can be expressed within
the framework of a neo-Kantian philosophy.

Ernst Cassirer's work is an interesting example of the
latter contention. Cassirer combined a unique knowledge
of the philosophical tradition with a thorough acquain-
tance with the history of science. Like Lasswitz, the his-
torian of Atomism, he was strongly influenced by Kant.
His main objective, also in some respects Lasswitz's, was
to show that the development of mathematics, including
the mathematical study of nature, causes a fundamental
turn in the way of thinking in epistemology. He held that
this change of perspective could be expressed within the
framework of a Kantian view of the problem of knowledge.
The notion of substance, a motive concept of metaphysics
since Aristotle, must be replaced by the mathematical
idea of function.[3]

Cassirer investigated relativity on the basis of this
viewpoint.[4] He felt that relativity theory was compatible

[1] See, for example, P. Jordan, *Anschauliche Quantentheorie*,
Berlin, 1936.

[2] See, for example, V. Fock, "Über die Deutung der Quantenmechanik," *Max Planck Festschrift*, p. 177, Berlin, 1958.

[3] See *Substance and Function* (1910), Dover edition, 1953;
*Das Erkenntnisproblem in der Philosophie und Wissenschaft der
neueren Zeit I-III*, Berlin, 1906–20.

[4] *Einstein's Theory of Relativity* (1921) (included in the Dover
edition of *Substance and Function*).

[15]

with neo-Kantian epistemology and illustrated and advanced the epistemological trend he had described. He pursued the same line of inquiry in his treatise on determinism and indeterminism in modern physics, a systematic and historical study of the concepts of causality and probability.[1] He showed that the meanings of these concepts have been closely connected with basic ontological doctrines. Cassirer found that quantum physics has also confirmed and deepened the transition from a substantialistic to a functional mode of thought.

The significance of Cassirer's work seems to lie especially in his emphasis on the depth of the contact between science and philosophy. Of particular importance is his view that the philosophical impact of quantum mechanics cannot be considered in isolation but must be looked upon as a step in an intellectual transformation brought about by development of the mathematical approach.

*　　*　　*

A fourth group of investigators of the philosophical foundations of quantum physics is the philosophers of science. Quantum physics met a situation in philosophy different from the one relativity theory encountered. The new philosophical movements that had been inspired by this theory and by developments in mathematical logic were now largely consolidated. When the quantal description entered the scene it found the philosophers of science apparently well prepared to cope with fundamental innovations in the description of nature. They had an arsenal of conceptual tools for logically analyzing its basic principles. In their view, the epistemological aspects of

[1] *Determinism and Indeterminism in Modern Physics*, New Haven, 1956.

the quantum issue were to be treated not within physics itself, but in the context of philosophy of science.

Philosophers of science have taken an attitude to quantum physics that is different from their attitude to relativity theory. On the whole they have not thought of the quantum situation as primarily a source of philosophical innovation, but have approached it more in the role of critic. From their standpoint, the disagreement between physicists about the proper interpretation of the quantal description—a disagreement obviously due more to epistemological than to physical factors—indicated that the situation in quantum physics was in need of a thorough philosophical analysis. The physicists' own efforts to clarify the situation were unsatisfactory because they lacked preparation. Philosophers of science have made several attempts to give quantum physics proper philosophical foundations.[1]

A typical example is the work by Reichenbach.[2] He compares the physicist's philosophy of quantum mechanics to the thin ice of a superficially frozen lake. To obtain a more satisfactory view it is necessary above all to analyze and revise the philosophical ideas about the existence of unobserved objects. The core of the interpretation problem is the relation between what Reichenbach calls phenomena, *i.e.* quantum occurrences that can be directly verified by amplification devices (clicks in a Geiger counter, spots on a photographic plate, tracks in

[1] See, for example, H. Reichenbach, *Philosophic Foundations of Quantum Mechanics*, Berkeley, 1944; G. Bergmann, "The Logic of Quanta," *American Journal of Physics* 15, 397 (1947); E. Kaila, "Zur Metatheorie der Quantenmechanik," *Acta Philosophica Fennica* 5 (1950).

[2] *Op. cit.*

[17]

a cloud chamber), and interphenomena, or all that happens in between phenomena. In Reichenbach's view the phenomenon–interphenomenon distinction is the quantum mechanical analogue of the ordinary distinction between observed and unobserved things.

There is more than one true description of unobserved objects. For example, we may say with equal justification that a tree becomes two trees, or that it disappears, or that it remains unaltered, when it is not observed. It is true that sometimes we may see the shadow without seeing the tree, but we may assume a change in the optical laws for unobserved objects, such that there is one shadow even if there are two trees or no trees at all. In classical physics, however, the class of equivalent descriptions of unobserved objects contains a so-called normal system, *i.e.* a system where the laws of nature, as well as the state of objects, remain the same whether the objects are observed or not.

Analogously, there is a class of equivalent descriptions of quantum mechanical interphenomena. In this class the interphenomena vary but the phenomena are invariant. However, in the quantum case the class does not contain a normal system. All interpretations of interphenomena entail "causal anomalies." For example, if we interpret electron interference experiments in terms of particles we must assume action at a distance. The particle and wave interpretation are "minimum systems," *i.e.* they deviate from a normal system as little as possible.

Interpretations that include only phenomena are called restrictive. They avoid causal anomalies, but only by ruling out certain statements. The Bohr–Heisenberg interpretation is an example; its restrictive rule is that only statements about measurable quantities, *i.e.* phenomena, are permitted, whereas statements about non-measurable quantities, *i.e.* interphenomena, are termed meaningless. For example, it is meaningless to say that the electron went through a particular slit on its way through the interferometer.

Reichenbach found the Bohr–Heisenberg restrictive rule unsatisfactory. This rule is simply a version of the quantum mechanical commutation relation and thus an expression of a physical law. But it expresses the law in semantic form, *i.e.* as a rule about the meaning of statements. Stated in such a form, it has to refer to a class of linguistic expressions which includes both meaningful and meaningless statements. It thus in a certain sense includes meaningless expressions in the language of physics.

Usually physical laws are not expressed in the meta-language but in the object language. In the case of the restrictive rule, Reichenbach proposed a formulation in which the statements were excluded not from the domain of meaning but from the domain of assertability. The idea was to introduce a trivalent logic containing the familiar truth values and a third category called indeterminate. This third truth value is associated with the group of statements that are called meaningless in the Bohr–Heisenberg interpretation.

*　　*　　*

The fifth and last group of contributions to the study of quantum physics' relation to philosophy claims that there is something philosophically new to be learned from the quantal description. The role of quantum physics in the history of ideas is compared to that of the scientific revolution following the Renaissance. It is asserted that the revisions of the foundations of physics caused by the quantum have exposed the narrowness of current conceptions of nature and have opened new possibilities for a more harmonious intellectual outlook. However, within this group too there are widely different views on the relation between quantum physics and the philosophical tradition.

Oppenheimer has discussed this question in his studies of the interaction between scientific discovery and "the common understanding."[1] He concludes that there are "deep, intimate, and subtle" connections between scientific findings and metaphysics and epistemology, but that these connections are not logically necessary. Findings in a special field may conflict with what philosophers have said about that field, but such findings cannot logically affect general philosophical doctrines. For example, the discovery that the constituents of matter are not entirely stable does not invalidate the doctrine that the true physical reality consists of immutable atoms. Scientific findings have no ontological bearings whatsoever; they do not lead to and they do not justify conclusions about the nature of reality. Quantum physics' general significance is that it has provided new instructive analogies to deep issues in the psychological and social sciences.

Heisenberg has approached the question from a different point of view. He argues that discoveries in natural science are significant for philosophy because they may let old philosophical problems appear in a new light. Quantum physics "touches very old trends of thought at many

[1] *Science and the Common Understanding*, New York, 1954. See also *The Open Mind*, New York, 1955 and "The Growth of Science and the Structure of Culture," *Daedalus*, Winter, 1958.

points, that it approaches some of the very old problems from a new direction."[1] Heisenberg is convinced furthermore that "in the history of human thinking the most fruitful developments frequently take place at those points where two different lines of thought meet."[2] Quantum physics and traditional philosophy are sufficiently related to be able to interact. They are interrelated primarily because the atomic problem has played such a central role in the history of philosophy.

Heisenberg has compared the development of the atomic idea in Greek philosophy with the development of atomic science in modern time.[3] He sees a parallel between the discussion on the nature of reality in Greek philosophy and in modern atomic physics. The shift from Democritus' extreme materialism to Plato's stress on mathematical form as the ultimate reality corresponds in some ways to the change from nineteenth-century Atomism to the present attempts to base the atomic structure of matter on a fundamental mathematical law.

Like most other students of the topic, Heisenberg finds that the area of strongest interaction between traditional philosophy and quantum physics is philosophy's central discipline, ontology.[4] He argues that the quantal description is incompatible with one of the most important ontological doctrines, *i.e.* Descartes' doctrine of the extended and thinking substance, and provides a counter-example

[1] *Physics and Philosophy*, New York, 1958, p. 187.

[2] *Ibid.*

[3] See also *Wandlungen in den Grundlagen der Naturwissenschaft*, Zurich, 1949; "Planck's Discovery and the Philosophical Problems of Atomic Physics," *On Modern Physics*, Heisenberg, Born, Schrödinger, Auger. London, 1961.

[4] See, especially, Ch. V of *Physics and Philosophy*.

[21]

to it. Consequently, the quantal description may affect the results of those philosophical schools that originated from a criticism of the Cartesian partition between mind and matter, and it can perhaps suggest new ways to overcome the difficulties of metaphysics and epistemology.

Heisenberg's claim that the quantal description violates the Cartesian view of physical reality is based on his analysis of the foundations of quantum physics. The main result of this analysis is that the quantum formalism cannot be regarded as a "description of nature" in the same sense as classical physics. This is because the so-called wave function or probability function which represents the state of a quantum system is not a completely objective quantity in the classical sense but contains a reference to the observer's knowledge of the system. In the quantum domain it is not possible to completely "objectivate" the description of phenomena. The key elements of the quantal description do not refer to actual fact but to possibility and tendency.

Thus, in Heisenberg's view quantum theory forcefully reminds us that natural science is made by man. It is not simply a symbolic representation of nature, but is part of the interplay between nature and man. What it describes is not nature as such, but nature as exposed to man's method of questioning. It makes Descartes' sharp separation between the world and the I impossible.

To characterize ontological doctrines less extreme than Descartes' metaphysical realism, Heisenberg uses the concept of objectivation. A statement is objectivated when it is claimed that its content does not depend on the conditions under which it can be verified. Practical realism, typical of natural science and our orientation in daily

[22]

life events, assumes that there are statements that can be objectivated. In terms of objectivation, the extreme ontological doctrine is dogmatic realism which claims that there are no statements concerning the material world that cannot be objectivated. According to Heisenberg, dogmatic realism is the position of classical physics and is incompatible with quantum physics.

The interaction between quantum physics and traditional philosophy is of course reciprocal. In particular, the difficulties in understanding the new description situation in the quantum domain have their main roots in our philosophical preconceptions. For example, the basis on which Einstein criticized quantum mechanics was the doctrine of dogmatic realism. To Einstein, the philosophical dictum that physical description is a conceptual representation of physical reality was one of the last ideas that a physicist should be prepared to give up, and Einstein could not accept a theory that contains statements that cannot be objectivated.

A remarkable feature of Heisenberg's argument is the extent to which it can be expressed in accustomed philosophical terms. This is particularly conspicuous when he confronts the new attitude to the problem of physical reality suggested by quantum mechanics with some of the philosophical doctrines of Empiricism and Criticism. As is well known, these doctrines resulted to a large extent from attempts to overcome difficulties afflicting metaphysical realism. Heisenberg's confrontation has put both the philosophical and the physical part of the problem into an interesting perspective. In particular, it may throw new light on the basic ideas in Kant's philosophical scheme.

The relationship between quantum physics and Kant's

philosophy had previously been investigated from a similar point of view by von Weiszäcker.[1] Central to his investigation is a comparison between the role of the synthetic judgements *a priori* in Kant's scheme and the role of the classical concepts in quantum theory. The former were considered conditions for human experience, the latter are considered conditions for describing physical phenomena.

This comparison strongly accentuates the problem of the status of classical concepts in the interpretation of quantum mechanics. Characteristically, Heisenberg does not try to give a definite philosophical answer to the problem. He regards the indispensability of the classical concepts as primarily a practical matter; their *a priori* is predominantly a practical one. Having been formed during the human mind's development in a very distant past, they are part of our cultural inheritance and we cannot and should not replace them, at least not at the present stage of knowledge. They are the indispensable tools for doing scientific work in our time. Heisenberg adds a few admittedly speculative but illuminating remarks on the question.[2] The *a priori* character of the classical concepts may be similar to that of the forms of behavior that in animal psychology are called inherited or innate schemes. It is quite plausible that for some primitive animals space and time are different from those of the species man. Further, the latter may not belong to the world independent of man.

A somewhat different view of the status of classical

[1] "Das Verhältnis der Quantenmechanik zur Philosophie Kants," *Die Tatwelt* **17**, 66 (1941) (included in *Zum Weltbild der Physik*, Stuttgart, 1957).

[2] *Physics and Philosophy*, p. 91.

concepts has been advocated by Rosenfeld.[2] He argues that the indispensability of these concepts in natural science and the restrictions in their applicability in atomic physics are in the last resort related to the size of the human brain and sense organs. Thinking and observation are claimed to be possible only in systems of such complexity that their size is macroscopic. The concept of a thinking being of atomic size is self-contradictory. All beings who are able to do physics will originally interact with the world only on the macroscopic scale, and they are bound to develop elementary concepts that are appropriate to phenomena on that scale. They will therefore be faced with a description problem when they begin to explore the world of atoms, and they will be forced to take recourse to a complementary mode of description.

In Rosenfeld's opinion the emergence of the complementary logic is not more accidental than the emergence of man himself as a product of organic evolution. It is in principle impossible to imagine some kind of minute Maxwellian demons who could describe the atomic world as directly as we human beings can describe the macroscopic world and thus free himself from complementarity restrictions. Our mental representation of processes in nature is dependent on our sensorium. In particular, the necessity that our brain be of macroscopic size is ultimately responsible for the conceptual peculiarities of quantum theory.

[2] "Foundations of Quantum Theory and Complementarity," *Nature* **190**, 384 (1961). See also "Strife about Complementarity," *Science Progress* No. 163, 393, (1953); "Misunderstandings Concerning the Principles of Quantum Theory," *Observation and Interpretation* (S. Körner, ed.), London, 1957.

However, this dependence on our sensorium does not introduce any subjective elements into science. True objectivity does not mean faithful conceptual reproduction of the phenomena independent of the observer, but rather the possibility of guaranteeing that the account of phenomena convey equivalent information to all observers. Yet, the human observer intervenes in a fundamental way by determining, at least to some extent, the language in which the laws of nature are formulated. These laws are significant not because they draw a picture of nature independent of who is looking at it, but rather because they reflect the interaction between ourselves and the external reality. This is completely in keeping with our position in the world and with the function of science. We are not merely contemplating the world; we are acting on it, and thereby modifying its course.

*   *   *

It can be seen from the contributions reviewed above that the way quantum physics has replaced the mechanical conception of nature is considered somewhat similar to the way post-Cartesian philosophical schools tried to solve the difficulties in Descartes' ontology. In both cases it was argued that the subject's role in "the process of knowledge" had been neglected. In philosophy attempts to clarify the role of the subject shifted the emphasis from ontology to epistemology. This shift revived old problems about the relation between things in themselves and phenomena, the meaning of objectivity, the formation of concepts, the scope and limits of human knowledge, etc. But the discussion remained within the old framework. The change was not so much a break with the ontological way of looking at our situation as a turn from the ontology

[26]

of nature to the ontology of the human mind. In physics, too, emphasis on the role of the observer has given prominence to epistemological problems, especially the status of the classical concepts. And here too the customary philosophical framework has usually been found adequate. No radically new philosophical point of view seems to have emerged from quantum physics.

Although the above review is far from exhaustive and may only indicate the trend of the author's views, one can hardly escape the conclusion that the discussion is still in a preliminary stage. It is difficult to find a balanced view of even the broad features of the topic, but its significance, and some of its peculiarities, have been brought out, especially by Heisenberg.

To analyze the topic further, it is useful to try to identify the principal limiting factors in the previous investigation. Obviously, the topic's partly logical and partly historical character impedes a balanced treatment. Also, many issues are involved that for centuries have been the object of intensive polemical debate. Further, it is difficult to give the topic a sufficiently well-defined structure because the philosophical doctrines are inherently vague. But none of these factors seem to be the main reason why the topic is still in such a preliminary state of investigation. The most important limiting factor may be lack of clarity about the topic's physical component. Our understanding of the foundations of quantum physics may not yet be sufficient to cope fully with the issues arising when the quantal description is confronted with ontological philosophy.

It is true that the Copenhagen interpretation of the quantal formalism has been very successful in clarifying measurement problems. The clarification of measurement problems has required a thorough analysis of physical concepts like position, time, momentum, energy, state, orbit, system, measuring apparatus, *etc.* But, interestingly enough, it has not required an equally thorough analysis of a concept like physical reality. The investigation of imaginary experiments has been focused on the concepts used by experimental physicists rather than on philosophical concepts. Further, the degree of clarity reached in measurement analysis seems to have depended on the possibility of avoiding an explicit discussion of the meaning of the fundamental ontological concepts. The separability of physical and philosophical concepts may also account in part for the lack of coherent discussion. For while most objections to the quantal description have been motivated by philosophy, they have generally been answered only on a physical plane.

The attempts to characterize the quantum situation in philosophical terms, *e.g.* to specify the status of reality and objectivity in the quantum domain, are much less satisfactory than the analysis of the physical concepts. Of course, these attempts derive partly from analysis of the foundations of quantum physics, but their principal source seems to be general philosophical attitudes whose connection with quantum physics is far from clear. It is doubtful that the current views of the philosophical aspects of quantum physics form an adequate basis for studying the meeting with traditional philosophy.

What is needed as a guide for this study is above all a concept or a viewpoint that fulfills two main conditions. In the first place it should be genuinely quantum mechanical and fundamental. Secondly, it should be close enough to the circle of traditional philosophical ideas to bring the two subjects in contact with each other and to

[28]

provide a perspective for assessing the nature of this contact.

One might have expected that the complementarity concept would present the natural basis for the study of the meeting between quantum physics and the philosophical tradition. Complementarity emerged early as a fundamental feature of the quantal description. It remained in the center of the discussion and was much refined. Further, its scope and significance have been illustrated by analysis of analogous situations in other fields. However, there are few clues to complementarity's relation to the ideas of traditional metaphysics and epistemology. As outlined above, Bohr held that the complementary mode of description is the proper technique to handle the epistemological problems engendered by the subject–object partition. This contention suggests that complementarity is deeply linked to the basic elements of traditional philosophy. But the details of this relationship are obscure, and therefore the complementarity concept does not seem to present a guide for studying quantum physics' meeting with the philosophical tradition.

These circumstances make it natural to reconsider the development of quantum theory to look for other characteristic elements that more readily reveal the contact between quantum physics and traditional philosophy. The principal aim of the following investigation is to show that the idea of correspondence is such an element. As is well known, the correspondence idea played a key role in the development of the matrix version of the quantal formalism and of the Copenhagen interpretation of quantum mechanics.

The correspondence idea concerns what is presumably the crux of the quantum issue: the relation between quantum and classical physics. One aspect of this relation had emerged already in the first stage of quantum physics, before the quantum of action was brought to bear on the nuclear model of the atom. Though Planck's radiation law rested on distinctly non-classical assumptions, it was not totally unconnected with classical theory. In a certain domain it yielded predictions which agreed with those obtained from the classical Rayleigh–Jeans radiation law. Bohr's quantum theory of the hydrogen spectrum, resting on the postulates of stationary states and indivisible transition processes, exhibited a similar asymptotic coincidence with the results of classical electron theory in the domain of large quantum numbers. While Bohr could use this limit property to express the Rydberg spectral constant in terms of the quantum and the electronic mass and charge, it did not seem initially to offer any clues to the further development of quantum theory.

However, a closer study of the structure of the radiation in the limit domain indicated that the relation between the two theories was not restricted to the rather obvious asymptotic coincidence. The outlines of a strikingly intimate "formal analogy" between the classical and the quantum scheme began to be visible. In the quantum theory of line spectra, this analogy manifested itself as a structural similarity of the quantal description of the spectrum and the classical description of the multiperiodic motion of the electron. There seemed to be a "correspondence" between quantum transitions and classical Fourier components, and this could be expressed in the Correspondence Principle which claimed that "the possibility of every transition process connected with the emission of radiation is conditioned by the presence of a

[30]

corresponding harmonic component in the motion of the atom."[1] Thus, the formal analogy seemed to suggest that the germs of quantum concepts like stationary states and individual transitions are in some sense already contained in the classical Fourier expression. In this way, the analogy became a tool for developing quantum theory: "The correspondence principle expresses the tendency to utilize in the systematic development of the quantum theory every feature of the classical theories in a rational transcription appropriate to the fundamental contrast between the [quantum] postulates and the classical theories."[2]

The correspondence approach proved its fertility by suggesting applications and extensions of the theory of line spectra, and the Copenhagen school came to regard the formal analogy as the principal guide to a coherent quantum theory. But the status of the correspondence principle and the meaning of the quantal-classical analogy were still obscure. For example, was the principle to be considered a third quantum postulate or did the analogy reflect a deep general feature of physical description?

Heisenberg's matrix mechanics and Born and Jordan's demonstration that this formalism is a mathematical generalization of classical Hamiltonian mechanics seemed to fulfill the program contained in the correspondence principle and to formulate precisely the meaning of the formal analogy. Mathematically, the idea of correspondence was now seen to have meant that the quantal formalism ought to emerge as a generalization of classical mechanics.

[1] N. Bohr, *Atomic Theory and the Description of Nature*, p. 37.
[2] *Ibid.*

The correspondence idea played a constructive role in more than the development of matrix mechanics. It also had a central position in the subsequent discussion, particularly in Bohr's work on the interpretation question. Bohr considered the symbolic mathematical forms as having a significance in theoretical physics beyond their use for expressing quantitative relationships. They provide "an essential means for the elucidation of the general qualitative points of view."[1] Accordingly, the chief aim of Bohr's work on the interpretation question was to express that quantum physics is "in every respect a generalization of the classical physical theories."[2]

Bohr concentrated on how the quantum generalization of the classical scheme is made possible and on the characteristics of this generalization. "It is the combination of features which are united in the classical mode of description but appear separated in the quantum theory that ultimately allows us to consider the latter as a natural generalization of the classical physical theories."[3] He introduced the word complementarity to describe the "relation of mutual exclusion characteristic of the quantum theory with regard to the application of the various classical concepts and ideas."[4] Yet seen from the standpoint of traditional philosophy, the most remarkable and interesting aspect of the quantum development may be not what its structure is and how the generalization was possible, but rather the very fact that the quantal description is a generalized mechanics. Similarly, the root of the interpretation controversy may not have been primarily the difficulty in encompassing complementary relationships within the traditional philosophical frame-

[1] *Op. cit.*, p. 8. [2] *Op. cit.*, p. 4. [3] *Op. cit.*, p. 19. [4] *Ibid.*

work, but rather the conflict between ontological philosophy and the very idea of a generalized description of nature.

Correspondence, in the sense used here, refers of course to a less specific characteristic of the quantal description than complementarity. But precisely because it emphasizes the concept of generalization itself rather than any particular feature of the quantum generalization, the correspondence idea seems suited to bring the meeting of quantum physics and traditional philosophy into sharper focus.

It may be argued that there is nothing fundamentally new in the correspondence idea, since mathematics has long ago made us familiar with the concept of generalization. Further, quantum mechanics is by no means the first use of a generalized conceptual scheme in physics. For example, non-Euclidean geometries preceded non-commutative algebra in physical theory. We have already mastered the philosophical problems raised by the contrast between ontology and generalized conceptual schemes. The relevant discussion took place in connection with relativity theory. Altogether, there is no longer any need to stress the philosophical significance of the generalization concept.

To find out to what extent the past discussion has actually clarified the issue would require a detailed investigation. Yet it is easy to see that we still do not adequately understand the description problems raised by a generalized mechanics. Our extreme difficulties in coming to grips with the situation in quantum physics are strikingly obvious from the forty year debate. It would seem that we can only construe the persistence of these difficulties as a sign that we still do not have a philosophical view in harmony with the present state of mathematical physics.

[33]

The following investigation has two main aims. First, it attempts to extract from the development of quantum physics as much information as possible about the epistemological meaning of the correspondence idea. Secondly, it attempts to apply this information to an assessment of quantum physics' relation to traditional philosophy.

The investigation proceeds from the view that our present understanding of the topic is much more primitive than is usually believed. The discussion will be fragmentary and tentative. Since the subject has deep historical roots, it seems useful to try to put the issues in a broad perspective. However, in the following the only purpose of a historical account is to bring into sharper focus the topic's logical aspects.

Chapter I is a brief description of some characteristics of the relation between science and philosophy, and an outline of the development of ontological philosophy. It serves to indicate the nature of the topic and to specify its philosophical component. Chapter II initiates the discussion of the physical component. It sketches the "classical" part of the history of Atomism, and especially seeks to bring out the atom concept's connection with the ontological form of thought and the severe logical difficulties that afflicted the concept during this phase of its history. Chapter III investigates the development of the correspondence idea in quantum physics. Its purpose is to show that this idea forms the epistemological core of the Copenhagen interpretation, and to ascertain the extent to which the interpretation discussion has clarified its meaning. Finally, Chapter IV attempts to utilize the material of the previous chapters for a discussion of quantum physics' relation to traditional philosophy.

[34]

I

Philosophical inquiry and scientific research form the main components of the effort to develop a so-called objective description of man's situation. While the sciences take advantage of the separability of problems and aim at an exhaustive account of limited domains of experience, philosophy focuses on our situation as a whole and seeks a global point of view, an overall perspective. Its aim is to formulate and answer the most general and the most fundamental questions.

Typical of the stepwise approach in the sciences is the idea that common knowledge and common language, though indispensable as the starting point, are not sufficient to provide an exhaustive and unambiguous description. Thus, studies of limited fields have been characterized by systematic efforts to accumulate more experience and to sharpen the conceptual tools. Philosophy has depended much less on new experience and concepts. Strangely enough, it seemed to be easier to find the entrance to the study of the general aspects of things than to the description of their special traits. Even after it had become apparent that the development of the sciences was a formidable task, the conviction prevailed that in philosophy everything could be accomplished by a few generations of thinkers or even by a single individual. Indeed it looked as if common knowledge and common language sufficed to identify the fundamental philosophical concepts and categories.

The distinction between philosophy and science reflects the idea that the study of fundamental features of our situation may be separated from the exploration of its details, and that the conditions for investigating general problems are different from those underlying the study of special problems. Yet throughout the history of ideas there has been an intimate and often dramatic interaction between philosophy and science. Although the character and implications of this interaction have become increasingly conspicuous in the course of the development of knowledge, many phases of it are still obscure.

The interrelation between the study of special fields of natural phenomena and the ways of conceiving of our situation as a whole is connected with one of the most remarkable features of Western philosophy. Our philosophical tradition was to a great extent generated by contemplation of issues later to be studied in science. The form of our philosophical thought grew out of attempts to establish a comprehensive view of nature. Although other problems, notably moral ones, played an important role, the motive concepts in our philosophy are physical, not social. Western philosophy not only includes a cosmology; it is written in a cosmological key. Had philosophical thought been more associated with questions of ethics or art than with questions like the status of ultimate reality and the validity of human knowledge, our general outlook might have been radically different.

The fact that our philosophy is primarily a philosophy of nature, and not one of, for example, the good life, has had many implications. Most important, philosophical ideas have influenced not only areas outside science. They have also colored our attitude towards science itself. The cosmological orientation of Western philosophy has provided a milieu very stimulating to the exploration of nature. For example, the bold idea, integral to our philosophical tradition, that nature as a whole is ruled by strict and immutable laws that can be discovered and expressed by man, must have been highly conducive to the study of natural phenomena.

Further, the purported cosmological character of the general and fundamental features of our situation suggested the view that part of the purpose of philosophy is to clarify the foundations of the description of nature. The sciences were supposed to rest on a philosophical basis. Philosophy was to characterize and delineate the various branches of science and to specify the relation between them. It was to provide categories and explanatory standards for scientific description. The essentials of a scientific theory were to be determined on philosophical criteria and expressed in philosophical terms.

The philosophical origin of many of the ideas used to understand natural phenomena has complicated the relation between frame and content in scientific description. It has also made it difficult to extend the scope and deepen the foundations of this description as experience accumulates. New theories cause previous explanatory standards to be reconsidered. The fact that these were not related in a simple way to previous experience but tied up to a global philosophical view has often made such reconsideration difficult. The same fact, however, has lent great significance to the exploration of nature. Because of the character of our philosophy, scientific theories have become a medium for formulating and illustrating philosophical doctrines. Findings in science have played an important

[37]

role in the attempts to overcome the difficulties in philosophy and to assess the various possible answers to the basic questions of reality and knowledge—answers that divide the philosophical schools. Thus they have had a direct bearing on our general outlook.

It is clear that under these conditions the periods when new light is shed on the conceptual framework in science not only mark out the great advances in our understanding of nature; they are also the milestones in the meeting between science and philosophy. Because science has proved to be evolutionary not only in its content but also, contrary to original expectations, in its form, *i.e.* evolutionary in the views and principles used to order and explain data as well as in the data themselves, science has emerged as an active agent in its relation to philosophy. It is above all the impact on our general outlook that make great scientific advances appear as "revolutions." Such periods may indeed be times of profound intellectual transformations.

Thus, the encounter between quantum physics and traditional philosophy does not raise a new type of problem in the history of ideas. Previous scientific advances have required similar investigations. For example, during the scientific revolution in the sixteenth and seventeenth centuries, the attempts to clarify the new approach to the description of nature included a thorough discussion of the relation between the new science of mechanics and the whole body of scholastic philosophy. This discussion was of great importance for recognizing the scope and depth of the intellectual transformation, and even helped to illuminate the foundations of mechanics. As long as we keep the present distinction between philosophy and science and retain the traditional conception of philo-

[38]

sophy, fundamental progress in either field is likely to influence the other.

* * *

The outstanding characteristic of Western philosophy is the unique significance ascribed to one concept: Being. Philosophical analysis focused on it already in Antiquity, and the cardinal philosophical problem came to be "What is the ultimate reality?" Ontology, the study of "being *qua* being," became the primary philosophical discipline that was to develop a comprehensive world view and provide the basis for all other fields of investigation.

Yet closer analysis of the concept of being and of the categories connected with it soon revealed unexpected difficulties. These difficulties have proved to be very stubborn, and philosophical debate has largely been a sequence of attempts to overcome them. For this reason philosophy is often called a field where the answers change but the questions remain the same. The horizons of Western philosophy were marked out long ago and they have been strikingly stable.

The following is an attempt to give a concise survey of the ontological form of thought and to show how strongly it has molded our philosophical tradition. From the outset, it must be kept in mind that ontological philosophy is not a well-defined system of concepts but rather a point of view or a mode of representing our situation. Its characteristics can hardly be exhibited except by historical examples.

The roots of the ontological view are perhaps as old as language itself. Practical orientation is set in a distinctly ontological key, and there are suggestive similarities between ontological philosophy and the efforts to represent man's situation through myths. The characteristics of the ontological style of thinking emerged in early Greek philosophy.

The enterprise that generated and molded Western philosophical thought apparently began as a program of a comprehensive natural history of the world. This program was envisaged by Anaximander. His aim was to obtain a complete account of all the world as it is. He regarded nature as one all-inclusive system that is ruled by immanent law, not by a supernatural being. The clue to nature's description is the concept of history. Anaximander held that living beings originated from inanimate matter, and that man had developed from animals of another kind. His "historia" included an account of the evolution of the cosmos of earth, sun, moon, and stars. At any time there is an indefinite number of such worlds which all arise from and pass away to a common reservoir. Anaximander called this reservoir "the unlimited" and considered it "a boundless expanse of infinitely different ingredients so thoroughly mixed together so as to be severally indiscernible in the mixture, but which when segregated from the mixture are recognizable as all the differences of an articulate world."[1]

Anaximander's successors focused their attention on the cosmological part of the "historia," and this led to a change in character of the original program. The idea was proposed by Anaximenes that all change results from a single mechanism: condensation-rarefaction. As air is compressed more and more, it becomes water and then earth. When it is rarefied, it becomes fire. The process

[1] Harold Cherniss, "The Characteristics and Effects of Presocratic Philosophy," *Journal of the History of Ideas* **12**, 319 (1951), pp. 324f.

of variation in density not only accounted for the formation of the world from the reservoir, now considered made up of extra-cosmic air, but explained all changes taking place in the world. This line of thought, reducing all change to a single process, was pursued by Heraclitus who drew some radical conclusions from it. He held that only the process really exists. All things are in constant flux because they are merely phases of the cosmic process.

Heraclitus was not interested in "historia" as such. "It is not natural phenomena but the *meaning* of them that one must comprehend if one is to achieve wisdom; wisdom, not information or learning, is the goal of man."[1] The new orientation of philosophical inquiry invited a distinction between the world of the senses and the world as it is in itself. Heraclitus did not yet distinguish between two kinds of being, but he did say that the senses are bad witnesses for those whose souls cannot understand their reports. The phenomenal world manifests a "hidden harmony" which binds all phases of the process together and renders the world intelligible. Since the soul is the clearest or highest phase of the world process, the meaning behind phenomena can be understood by introspection.

The most significant step in transforming Anaximander's project of natural history into ontological philosophy was taken by Parmenides. As is well known, he argued that change is impossible, and based the argument entirely on the notion of being. Being *is*, and non-being *is not*. Consequently, that which *is* must be stable, ingenerable, indestructible, homogeneous and continuous. The necessity that a thing be identical with itself implies that it cannot change into something else. This argument,

[1] *Op. cit.*, p. 332.

[41]

which seemed to be inescapable, acted like an intellectual earthquake.

The Presocratic thinkers made several attempts to answer Parmenides' challenge. One attempt was to posit the existence of a limited number of Parmenidean Beings, physical bodies and agents to move them, and account for all change and variety in nature by the mingling of these "roots." This emphasis on the mixing process brought up the question as to whether the roots have minimal parts. Denial of this led to the assumption of an infinitude of entities or qualities and to the idea that everything contains something of everything else. Conversely, the Atomists assumed that all matter consists of indivisible particles, and denied the reality of all qualities except size, shape and motion of the atoms. The Atomists' doctrine entailed an assumption very difficult to accept from an ontological point of view: the existence of the void.

Parmenides' question: what is Being? gradually became the central issue of philosophy. The philosophical discipline dealing with it was called ontology, *i.e.* the study of being. The question was usually interpreted as: what is really real? It is difficult to formulate clearly the meaning of this question. A vivid description of the tendency behind it has been given by Eddington.[1] He remarks that words like "existence," "substance" and "reality," when employed in books on philosophy, are hard to understand because they are used as if they are endowed with some kind of celestial halo. Philosophers generally use the word reality "with the intention of evoking sentiment. It is a grand word for a peroration. 'The right honorable speaker went on to declare that the

[1] *The Nature of the Physical World*, London, 1928, Ch. 13.

concord and amity for which he had unceasingly striven had now become a reality (loud cheers).' The conception which it is so troublesome to comprehend is not 'reality' but 'reality (loud cheers).'"[1] The same peculiar tendency is visible in the ontological definition of "substance" as that which is in itself, is independent of everything else, is self-supporting, uncaused, and ultimate. It is also apparent in expressions like "the existing reality of Nature," or in the answer the biblical God is said to have given when asked for his name: "I am who am and he who is."[2]

Contemplation of the problem of Being has generated much of the philosophical discussion and terminology. The various philosophical schools are distinguished mainly by their answers to the question: what is the nature of the primordial elements of the universe? There has seemed to be no completely satisfactory criteria to decide this question. Two broad answers have been proposed and constitute the two major schools in ontological philosophy. The Materialist school, originating with the Ionian philosophers, claims that the ground of Being is matter and that all natural phenomena are manifestations of matter in motion. The Idealist school, which originated with the Pythagoreans and whose most famous representative was Plato, holds that Being is rooted, not in matter, but in number, forms, ideas or some spiritual substance. Within the two schools there are divergent branches. Among the Materialists, a notable issue of controversy has been the nature of the laws governing the motion of matter. In Idealism, it is common to distinguish between, *e.g.* subjective and objective versions.

[1] *Op. cit.*, Everyman's Library Edition, p. 273.
[2] *Exodus* III, 13–14.

The various answers that have been given to the question of the ultimate constituents of the universe have all seemed to entail difficulties. It has been characteristic of these difficulties that while they were suggested by the basic question, no guide to their solution appeared to be at hand. They could neither be settled, nor could they be ignored. Their presence was a strong motivation for philosophical analysis, but their persistence made philosophy static. Most important, they did not seem to originate from insufficient knowledge. Additional knowledge appeared to be completely incapable of affecting the situation. Thus, the philosopher could either hope that his puzzles might be clarified by further philosophical analysis, or believe that they are inherent in our situation, forever unsolvable.

The most impressive attempt to create an all-inclusive description of our situation on the basis of the notion of being is perhaps the Aristotelian system of thought. Aristotle himself considered his philosophy the climax of a long development during which his general formulation and solution of the fundamental problems had been prepared. For him the distinctive feature of philosophy was that it studies being *qua* being. Consequently, its principles are those which hold for everything that is real. Philosophy contains the presuppositions for all the sciences, since it concerns that which is first in reality, *i.e.* that whose presence is necessary for all the rest of reality. None of the special sciences deal with being as being. They isolate parts of being and investigate the attributes of these parts. Physics deals with motion; mathematics with quantity; biology with life. They deal, not with unqualified being, but with being only as motion, quantity or life.

To Aristotle, "the ancient and everlasting question: what is being? really amounts to: what is substance?"[1] He considers substance as that which in any individual thing so to say stands under or supports its qualities. Substance is the primary mode of being; it is primary in definition, in knowledge and in time. Each individual thing is specified by some determinations which belong to all that has being. It is the task of philosophy to enumerate and study these determinations or categories. There are ten of them, and the fundamental category is substance. The other categories, the accidents, which include quantity, quality, space and time, derive their meaning from the concept of substance and thus are not independent beings, but beings *via* something else. The ten categories define the range of possible determinations of reality. Aristotle distinguished between matter and form and between potential and actual being. Those attributes of an object that are essential for its existence are called its substantial form. A thing is potentially that which it can become, and actually that which it is. Motion is a transition from potential to actual being. In general, every change is the actualization of a form.

Strong doubts regarding the soundness of the ontological approach might have erupted when the study of mechanical phenomena gradually made it clear that the philosophical categories on which physics was to be based were inadequate to describe consistently even the simplest phenomena in inanimate nature. It is indeed remarkable that the apparently coherent and harmonious Scholastic system which through centuries had been so uniquely influential and in which Aristotelian doctrines

[1] *Metaphysics* I, 68.

[45]

had been much refined and developed, was made intellectually obsolete, not by subtle new insights into the position of man, but by bringing into proper focus the very simplest aspects of natural phenomena. However, although mechanics changed the relation between science and philosophy, it did not radically alter the concept of philosophical inquiry. Despite a feeling that human reason had been corrupted by the School, the adequacy of the ontological mode of thought was not called in question.

Remarkably, the new methods in physics seemed to be fully compatible with ontological ideas. The transition from Aristotelian to Newtonian physics could be viewed in an ontological context, and described simply as the introduction of a new ontology: a qualitative, hierarchical world had been replaced with a quantitative geometro-mechanical universe.[1] Nevertheless, it is important to keep in mind that the ensuing attempts to survey our situation on the basis of mechanics were not simply an extrapolation of the mechanical description. Rather, the mechanical conception of nature is a product of mechanics' encounter with an ontologically oriented philosophy. In this respect, it corresponds to Plato's mathematical ontology which was the result of the meeting of mathematics and philosophy in Antiquity.

However, even though the new start in philosophy remained within the frame of the ontological approach, the mechanical conception of nature accentuated some of the difficulties of ontology. These difficulties became the main object of philosophical analysis in the following centuries. They were not raised by mechanics itself. Mechanics gave them a particular expression but it did not

[1] See, for example, A. Koyré, *From the Closed World to the Infinite Universe*, New York, 1958.

[46]

create them. They originated from the ontological approach, and they had already been discussed by ancient philosophers.

If one were committed to a geometro-mechanical ontology, and thus held that the ground of being is matter moving in space according to mechanical laws, one had to face the problem of the ontological status of all the entities that seemed to exist but could not be encompassed in the accepted class of ultimate constituents of reality. Mechanics, when viewed through an ontological lens, seemed to imply that some qualities are more real than others. The so-called primary qualities, which could be specified by mechanical parameters, appeared to constitute the primordial elements of the universe. The reality of the secondary qualities seemed to raise a fundamental problem. Further, an account of biological, psychological and social phenomena on a purely materialistic basis appeared to be compounded with unsurmountable difficulties. An idealist ontology, based on the assumption that the universe is ultimately of a spiritual nature or that its real constituents are imponderable, mental or ideal, made the ontological status of matter acute. If one adopted, instead of a monist conception, a dualist or pluralist point of view, and assumed that reality is made up of several different kinds of entities, *e.g.* a thinking as well as an extended substance, one had to face problems about the relationship, especially the interaction, between the various substances.

The efforts to solve these difficulties took two main directions. One was a series of attempts to improve ontology. Spinoza proposed a single substance which has an extended as well as a thinking mode of being, and Leibniz postulated that reality is made up of "monads" which

[47]

are distinguished solely by their varying degrees of activity. Such proposals had little impact on subsequent discussion. More influential was the attempt to overcome the narrowness of the mechanical conception of reality by combining Democritus' materialism with Heraclitus' view that all evolution is generated by a fight between opposites, or that strife is the cause of all things.

In an idealist context, the Heraclitian view had been introduced into post-Renaissance philosophy by Hegel. The theme of his monumental scheme is the so-called absolute spirit's gradual awakening or becoming conscious of itself. The process of awakening, which is the world process, is not mechanical, but Heraclitian or "dialectical." To illuminate the meaning of this term Hegel developed a body of doctrines, a dialectics. The dialectical laws govern all of nature: the "motion" of thought as well as the motion of matter. Matter is the negation of spirit, and is as such a necessary component of the dialectical process through which the universal spirit unfolds itself. In Dialectical Materialism, the primary constituent of being is claimed to be matter instead of a universal spirit, but the idea is retained that the basic laws of evolution are dialectical and not mechanical. In contrast to mechanical processes, the dialectical "motion" of matter gives rise to ontologically new forms and qualities in the course of time. The evolution takes place in stages, and while its fundamental law is dialectical, the laws of motion are different for each stage of matter's development. Protein molecules and the associated qualities of life and consciousness represent the temporary climax of this development. Dialectical materialism is a comprehensive world view embracing all phenomena. It maintains that the same dialectical laws, which rule the

[48]

evolution of nature, govern the development of human society and even human knowledge.

The philosophical ideas reviewed above may be regarded as a direct continuation of the Presocratic line of thought. However, the second direction taken by the efforts to overcome the difficulties attached to the mechanical conception of nature led to a change of perspective. In this development, discussion came to be concerned more with the so-called problem of knowledge than with the problem of being. Epistemology, the theory of knowledge, took the place of ontology, the theory of being, as the most important philosophical discipline. Yet, this was by no means a break with the ontological approach. It was only a shift of emphasis from the object to the subject, from the ontology of the world to the ontology of the mind.

Considered from a simple ontological standpoint, the problem of knowledge presents itself in a straightforward way. The knowing subject is part of the inventory of the universe, and its nature is determined by the basic ontological assumptions. In the old materialist tradition, the soul was considered a subtle kind of matter. Aristotle regarded the human soul as the substantial form of the human body. Scholasticism retained this view, but added that, unlike other substantial forms, the human soul is of a spiritual nature and is therefore able to be actual without inhering in matter. In Descartes' dualistic scheme, the mind was considered a separate thinking substance.

Similarly, from an ontological point of view, the subject–object relation is just a part of the whole scheme of being. The process of knowledge, although important, is merely one of the various processes taking place in the

[49]

universe. Simple analogies were commonly used to describe the process of knowledge. Reality leaves an imprint on the mind like a seal on wax. The mind is like a spectator following a drama on a stage. The ordinary eye perceives things; the "mind's eye" perceives ideas. Accordingly, ideas are mental copies of things in the world. Our mental picture of the world is related to reality as a map to the terrain itself. True knowledge is like a good map, a faithful representation of reality.

Locke, the founder of the Empiricist school, made the human mind the focus of philosophical analysis, and contrary to expectation this shift of emphasis was to strongly accentuate some of the peculiar difficulties of ontological philosophy. Locke held that in order to make progress in philosophy it was necessary to develop a genuinely empirical science of human nature. The task of this new science was to describe the "physiology" of the human mind and thus to clarify its nature, powers and limitations. The epistemologist was to explain the working of the human mind as Newton had explained the working of nature. Since one must understand an instrument if one is to use it properly, the starting point in philosophy should be the investigation of our mental tools. The epistemologist was to become a mental physiologist who drew up an inventory of the human mind and studied its operations.

Locke envisaged that his program might involve difficulties, but he thought they would be merely of a practical sort. Of course, the mind is normally not aware of itself and of its ways of working, and it is not easy for it to step aside and observe itself. It requires art and pains to make the mind its own subject of investigation, but doing mind physiology is not in principle different from

[50]

doing body physiology. In some ways, it is even easier to study the construction of the mind than to investigate the body's organs. In particular, the mind seems more immediately accessible to exploration than the body.

The Empiricists' assumptions about the construction and functioning of the human mind were as simple as those underlying the ancient theories of cognition. Locke assumed that, besides mechanically interacting material bodies, the world consists of immaterial substances capable of perception and cognition. The mind is a receptacle of ideas just as the universe is a receptacle of bodies. The basic components of the human mind are the senses and the understanding. At birth the mind is like an "empty cabinet" or a "white paper void of all characters." The function of the senses is to "let in" the material which is to be processed by the understanding. This material is "stamped upon," "imprinted on" or "engraven in" the mind. The understanding can analyze it into its constituents, and from these synthesize compound ideas.

Clearly, the nature and scope of human knowledge are dependent on the sensory channels and the understanding's way of processing the data. The inlets to the mind might have been different in character, number and capacity. God could have made us with other sense organs. Likewise, the understanding might have used other methods of handling the sensory material than those it actually employs. Since we can have no ideas that our faculties are unable to give us, we are shut off from contemplating how creatures in other parts of the universe, and better endowed than we, might view things. Moreover, we are kept in ignorance of many things we can conceive of. One of the principal limitations of our knowledge arises from the fact that we are destitute of senses

[51]

acute enough to perceive the corpuscles of which all bodies are composed, even though we have ideas of the primary qualities of matter. "I doubt not but if we could discover the figure, size, texture and motion of the minute constituent parts of any two bodies, we should know without trial several of their operations one upon another; as we do now the properties of a square or a triangle."[1]

Such limitations indicated the mediocrity of the human intellectual equipment. However, Locke's investigation pointed to even more severe shortcomings which seemed to call in question the feasibility of the whole approach and the very possibility of a coherent theory of knowledge within an ontological context. For example, even though ideas are brought into the mind in a way that prevents us from obtaining an idea of substance, we nevertheless presuppose substance as the "substratum" or "support" of the ideas we obtain through the senses. Further, it is claimed that ideas of primary qualities are authentic copies of such qualities in the material world, but no justification for this claim can be given on the basis of the empirist conception of the process of knowledge. Locke took a calm view of this state of affairs. He concluded from his survey of the powers of the human mind that "the Candle that is set up in us shines bright enough for all our purposes."[2] The understanding which "sets man above the rest of sensible beings"[3] is very inferior to a perfect comprehension of reality. In most areas we can have no knowledge and must be satisfied with opinion.

[1] *An Essay Concerning Human Understanding*, Book IV, Ch. III, §25.
[2] *Ibid.*
[3] *Ibid.*

Berkeley interpreted the situation differently. Like Locke, he began his investigation of human knowledge by commenting on the strange condition that had afflicted philosophy. This subject has been filled with paradoxes, difficulties and inconsistencies. If we follow the light of reason we seem to end in forlorn scepticism. This is not because things are obscure or our understanding imperfect. The fault is not with our faculties but in the wrong use we make of them. The difficulties embarrassing the mind are of our own making. "We have first raised a dust and then complain that we cannot see."[1]

In Berkeley's opinion, the philosophical puzzles had a common root: misuse of the verb "to exist." The only entities which can in an ontological sense be said to exist are spirits, *i.e.* "active beings" with the faculty of perception and thought. There are no entities in the universe other than perceiving and thinking souls. An unthinking, passive, innate, inert substance, as presupposed by the materialists, is an impossibility. The materialists introduced such fictitious entities because they did not grasp the meaning of the concept of existence when applied to passive entities.

For passive entities, to exist is the same as to be perceived by a spirit, whether a human mind or God. An object does not cease to exist when unperceived by a human mind, because it is continually perceived and thus kept in being by God. "The table I write on I say exists; *i.e.* I see and feel it: and if I were out of my study, I should say it existed; meaning thereby that if I were in my study, I might perceive it, or that some other spirit actually does perceive it. There was an odor, that is, it

---

[1] *A Treatise Concerning the Principles of Human Knowledge, I,* §3.

was smelt; there was a sound, that is, it was heard: a color or figure, and it was perceived by sight or touch. This is all that I can understand by these and the like expressions . . . . As it is impossible for me to see or feel anything without an actual sensation of that thing, so it is impossible for me to conceive in my thoughts any sensible thing or object distinct from the sensation or perception of it. All those bodies which compose the mighty frame of the world have no subsistence without a mind."[1]

To the view that, even though ideas themselves do not exist without mind, there might be copies of them existing in an unthinking substance, Berkeley remarks: "An idea can be like nothing but an idea; a color or figure can be like nothing but another color or figure. Again I ask whether those supposed originals or external things of which our ideas are the pictures or representations be themselves perceivable or no? If they are, then they are ideas and we have gained our point; but if you say they are not I appeal to anyone whether it be sense to assert a color is like something which is invisible; hard or soft like something which is intangible and so of the rest. It is plain that the very notion of what is called matter or corporeal substance involves a contradiction in it."[2] He pointedly adds, "even if we give the materialists their external bodies, they by their own confessions, are never nearer knowing how their ideas are produced since they are unable to comprehend in what manner a body can act upon spirit or how it is possible it should imprint any idea on the mind."[3]

On Berkeley's ontological assumptions, what kind of knowledge can an active being have of another active

[1] *Ibid.*   [2] *Op. cit.*, §8.   [3] *Ibid.*

being? Berkeley says that one can have no ideas of a spirit, but one can have "notions." Our knowledge of other minds is based on analogy.

Berkeley is usually considered a main protagonist of philosophical Idealism. His emphasis on the primacy of spiritual substance and his assertion that matter has no existence independent of mind had a strong impact. His investigation showed how difficult it is to combine the subject–object problem harmoniously with the ontological approach. The doctrine that everything is in a certain sense in the mind—a doctrine which Berkeley considered to be in accordance with common sense—raised many puzzling problems, not least concerning the relation between a psychological and a physical description.

Hume continued the Empiricist discussion of the problem of knowledge. According to his ontology, the mind consists entirely of perceptions. These are of two kinds, impressions and ideas. Impressions, *i.e.* sensations, feelings, emotions are distinguished from ideas only by being more vivid and distinct. The fundamental epistemological problem is to investigate ideas, and the aim is to ascertain which impressions correspond to the idea under investigation. Complex ideas are built up of simple ones, and to all simple ideas there correspond simple impressions.

Hume's distinction between the raw material furnished by the senses and the understanding's corresponding ideas or concepts made clearer the structure of philosophical problems as conceived by the Empiricists. Since the sensory basis is a bundle of distinct impressions, the fundamental question is: how can the mind establish any ties between them? Hume analyzed the idea of causality, but could find no impressions corresponding to it. It cannot be seen from the constitution of the reservoir of impressions that something must happen because something else is happening. Experience only can teach us what is, not what must be. The idea of causal necessity cannot be anchored in experience, but is a product of imagination. Although this idea may be indispensable, it is from a rational point of view no more than a habit. Causality is nothing but constant conjunction.

This view has far-reaching consequences. There is no reason why anything should not produce anything else. For all we can know, matter may very well produce thought. Any object may be annihilated in the next moment. To Newton, gravitational action at a distance seemed somehow less rational than action by contact. But to Hume it was as easy to accept one as the other, since according to his doctrine, impact between bodies as a cause of motion is as mysterious as gravitational attraction.

The structure of our intellectual equipment shows that we can make two fundamentally different sorts of inquiries. One is inquiry into matters of fact or existence; the other is investigation of relations between ideas. We can have no knowledge of relations between empirical phenomena, only belief or opinion. The contrary of a matter of fact can always be imagined and therefore is always possible. Anything in the world of existence might have been different from what it is. Knowledge pertains only to the world of ideas. Here, deductive reasoning is possible. Mathematical relationships are proved by comparing ideas, and in no way depend on what exists in the universe. Mathematical necessity is the only kind of rational necessity known to us, and because it is known to us we can establish that it is absent from the empirical world of facts.

From the beginning, the Empiricist school had been strongly influenced by mechanics. The aim was to do for the mind what mechanics had done for the universe. It is interesting that Hume, its most prominent representative, was led to emphasize the limitations of the new science: "While Newton seemed to draw off the veil from some of the mysteries of nature he showed at the same time the imperfections of the mechanical philosophy; and thereby restored her ultimate secrets to that obscurity in which they ever did and ever will remain."[1]

Hume's analysis of the human intellectual equipment brought him into a state of mind of acute intellectual discomfort. He found himself surrounded by a darkness where it was not possible to give rational reasons for believing anything. "There are two principles which I cannot render consistent; nor is it in my power to renounce either of them; namely that all our distinct perceptions are distinct existences and that the mind never perceives any real connection among distinct existences. Did our perceptions either adhere in something simple and individual or did the mind perceive some real connections among them there would be no difficulty in the case. For my part, I must plead the privilege of a sceptic and confess that this difficulty is too hard for my understanding."[2]

It is interesting to compare the course of the Empiricist philosophy of knowledge with the development of the Presocratic program of a natural history. Anaximander wanted a comprehensive description of the world. Locke

---

[1] *History of England*, Ch. LXXI (quoted by N. Kemp Smith in *The Philosophy of David Hume*, London, 1949, p. 58).
[2] *Treatise on Human Nature*, Appendix.

[57]

envisaged a complete physiology of the mind. Both undertakings were halted by the discovery of peculiar difficulties. The attempts to cope with these difficulties altered the original character of the projects. They changed from a historical, descriptive account of natural phenomena into an analysis of the problem of being and the problem of knowledge. The reasoning of Parmenides and Hume, in many respects strikingly similar, presented a formidable challenge to later thinkers.

Plato's and Aristotle's metaphysics were monumental answers to the question of the structure of being. Kant's *Critique of Pure Reason* is an equally monumental answer to the question of the structure of knowledge. Kant's system is as rich as Aristotle's. Like Aristotle, Kant felt that the problem he set out to solve had gone through a long period of preparation and was now ripe for its final solution. He saw the history of philosophy as a directed approach to his own standpoint.

As regards the question of the structure and function of the mind, there are two main differences between the Empiricists and Kant. Kant considered the structure of the mind as much more ramified than they did, and he took a different view of its role in the process of knowledge. According to Kant, the weakness of their analysis is that it rests on a wrong conception of the situation of the human mind in the process of its obtaining knowledge of nature. The Empiricists pictured it as a pupil who listens to a teacher. Instead, human reason should be compared to an appointed judge who compels the witness to answer questions which he has himself formulated. Kant compares this shift of view to the introduction of purposeful experimentation in physics "which entered the study of nature on the pure path of science after having for so many centuries been nothing but approaches of merely random groping."[1]

Kant accepted Hume's argument that concepts like causal necessity cannot be anchored in the sensory material, but he maintained that such concepts still have a rational basis. They are rooted in reason itself. Kant believed that he could give a complete solution to Hume's problem by undertaking a critical examination of pure reason. In this way an exhaustive list of metaphysical concepts, including causal necessity, could be furnished, and the content, scope and limits of metaphysics could then finally be marked off. Kant did not discuss in detail how reason is to bring to light its own architecture. One has the impression that he considered Newton's method applicable also to such a task. In other words, the aim is to derive the "causes" from the study of phenomena; to derive the construction of human reason, as of a machine, by studying it at work.

The most important feature of the ontological part of Kant's philosophy is his distinction between the world of things as they are in themselves, and the world of phenomena, or things as they appear to us. Human reason is a lawgiver, but it can legislate only for phenomena, not for things in themselves. If we are to make a "Copernican turn" and maintain that objects must conform to knowledge, instead of vice versa, the objects must be objects of the senses, and not objects in themselves.

It is typical of Kant's approach that instead of regarding the distinction between the intelligible and the sensible world as a mere restriction, he should exploit it and show that here too a limitation is a source of strength. Knowledge is restricted to phenomena, but phenomena, in turn,

[1] *Critique of Pure Reason*, Preface to Second Edition (trans. N. Kemp Smith), London, 1958, p. 20.

[59]

bear the stamp of the human intellectual equipment. We can have no knowledge whatsoever about things in themselves or how they are related to phenomena. We can know phenomena and, since some aspects of them are rooted in ourselves, part of our knowledge is even *a priori*, *i.e.* independent of experience. Thus, phenomena are conditioned by our way of knowing. Things in themselves are unconditioned. This makes room for those aspects of our situation which are outside the scope of rational knowledge, *e.g.* morality. We are members of two worlds. In the world of phenomena, the will is subject to the law of causality. But as a thing in itself it is not subject to that law, and is therefore free. Freedom is not a rational notion, yet neither is it contradictory. Morality presupposes freedom, but we need not understand this notion. It is enough to see that it does not contradict itself.

The human intellectual equipment is characterized by the partition between the senses and the mind (the sensibility and the understanding). Knowledge comes from their union. An object is given to us, intuited, through the sensibility whose forms are space and time. The object given by intuition is thought by the understanding which judges and synthesizes by means of its reservoir of pure concepts or categories. We have no reason to believe that our intellectual faculties are the only possible ones. It is only from the human standpoint that we can speak about space and time, and perhaps only man's understanding has twelve categories. Even the distinction between sensibility and understanding may be peculiar to the human race. But we cannot form a conception of other possible intellectual faculties.

Just as Aristotle was convinced that he had given a complete account of the basic structure of being, Kant held that his critique of pure reason exhausted the subject. He thought he had finally overcome the scandal in philosophy created by Hume's inability to refute the sceptic. He believed that man's situation was now fully understood in its main features. In particular the mathematical description of nature, Newtonian physics, had obtained a rational and immutable foundation. The parallel between Aristotle and Kant extends to the way in which their doctrines were superceded. The discoveries that made the inadequacy of critical philosophy particularly clear came from the same unexpected side as those which invalidated the Aristotelian system, the study of simple natural phenomena.

II

When viewed from a historical perspective, quantum physics appears as the temporary climax of a development begun in Antiquity by the same thinkers who laid the foundations of Western philosophy. This development has centered on the issue of stability and change. Its main concern has been to clarify why the objects in nature are so remarkably permanent and have such characteristic properties. Before quantum physics, the discussion of this problem had passed through two stages, a speculative and an empirical. With quantum physics the discussion entered what may be called its logical stage: the problem was brought within the grasp of an algorithm, the quantal formalism.

Through its entire history, the study of the question of nature's stability and specificity has been one of the most vital areas of contact between physics and philosophy. The ways of approaching the question have not only determined the attitude to the foundations of physical science; they have also strongly influenced and been influenced by metaphysics and epistemology. Thus, from a historical point of view, the partial clarification of the stability question's logical basis may be expected to have important bearings on the relation between physics and philosophy.

Presocratic philosophy focused attention on problems concerning the variety, permanence and transformations of natural forms and found that there is no obvious clue

[62]

to these problems.[1] The various formulations and answers suggested gave direction to subsequent developments in philosophy and physics. Common to them was the view that creation and annihilation are impossible in an ontological sense, *i.e.* that change does not involve genesis and destruction. Guided by this view, the early philosophers looked for unifying principles to interpret the diversity of processes in nature. For example, Anaximenes attempted to base the description of nature on the single mechanism of condensation-rarefaction and Empedocles tried to account for all natural phenomena as quantitative variations of four qualitatively different unchangeable elements.

It is very interesting that the logical core of the problem of stability and specificity was seen already at the speculative stage of the discussion. A school of Greek thinkers proposed that the concept of indivisibility or atomicity contains the key to the problem. According to this school, nature's stability is due to a limitation of the divisibility of matter. All ordinary things are compound bodies and their properties reflect the characteristic size, shape, configuration and motion of their ultimate units. All transmutations in nature are to be explained in terms of aggregation, dispersion or rearrangement of the unchangeable atoms of which everything is composed.

Early Atomism was deeply immersed in the discourse typical of Greek philosophy. The atomic idea is usually attributed to Leucippus.[2] His aim was to reconcile pre-

[1] See, for example, John Burnet, *Early Greek Philosophy*, London, 1930; Harold Cherniss, "The Characteristics and Effects of Presocratic Philosophy," *Journal of the History of Ideas* 12, 319 (1951).

[2] For the history of the early phases of Atomism, see, for example, Cyril Bailey, *The Greek Atomists and Epicurus*, Oxford, 1928.

ceding conflicting views, and especially to overcome the fundamental difficulties pointed out by Parmenides in explaining multiplicity and change. Each atom indeed possesses all the characteristics of the famous Parmenidean "One": it is ingenerable, indestructible, indivisible and homogeneous. Thus, judged on the contemporary philosophical background, Leucippus' crucial step consisted in introducing a new concept of reality by positing the existence of a non-material entity, the void, which separates the atoms and makes it possible for them to move.

From a physical standpoint, the atomic hypothesis' value is its simplicity, visualizable character, and explanatory power. A typical example is the simple atomic interpretation of the solid, fluid and gaseous state of matter and of processes like melting, freezing, evaporation and condensation. Since the attributes of the atoms were regarded as well defined and numerically expressible, and since atomic motions were supposed to be regulated by strict causality, physics, if based on the atomic idea, was to be an exact, quantitative and deterministic science.

The assumption of an atomic structure of matter brings a "scale" into the description of nature. Notions like small and large, slow and fast, light and heavy, are no longer mere conventions but acquire an absolute significance when expressed in atomic units. Further, the view that atoms retain their individuality, that change does not go all the way through in transmutations, introduces a peculiar idea of "completion" into physics. In essential respects, nature is not inexhaustible. There is not only a limit to the degree of subdivision of a piece of matter; there is also a limit to what happens in nature. The simplest form of the atomic hypothesis implies that nothing happens except displacements of atoms.

[64]

In the context of Ancient Greek philosophy, the idea that only the atoms and the void have true existence suggested a completely materialistic and deterministic concept of nature. Such a comprehensive view that explained even cosmological, biological, psychological and social phenomena in terms of material atoms moving according to strict laws was created in outline by Democritus. This view articulated the philosophical doctrine based on a materialistic ontology and causal necessity, a doctrine that was to become one of the most influential positions in Western philosophical thought.

Yet, Atomism and the associated mechanical conception of nature were never dominant in Antiquity. They were criticized partly from an ontological and partly from a logical point of view. The contrast between the sensible world with its multiplicity of qualities and the world of atoms with no qualities except size, shape and weight presented many ontological difficulties. Universal determinism, excluding freedom and purpose from the natural world, seemed in sharp conflict with the human condition. Most important, however, the limitation of the divisibility of matter seemed a manifest logical contradiction. The words used to characterize the atomic attributes and to distinguish one kind of atom from another belong to a description based on the notion of continuity. A sphere can be divided and its parts are not themselves spheres. If the atoms of fire are spherical, then they are not indivisible and their parts are not themselves fire.

The logical difficulties inherent in atomicity and continuity had been acutely pointed out by Zeno. On account of these difficulties Atomists often took recourse to the view that the notion of a least possible material body was to be understood in a physical, not a mathematical, sense.

[65]

Atoms are indivisible because they are uncuttable, compact, impenetrable, rigid. They cannot be divided because they cannot be acted upon, and they cannot be acted upon because they are so hard. This was sufficient to save the atomic idea as a fruitful means of accounting for the properties and reactions of substances, but it did not put atomic theory on a satisfactory logical basis. The argument derived from an attitude to the relation between physics and mathematics that seemed adequate in the early stages of science. However, with the mathematization of the description of nature, this attitude has proved increasingly inadequate and has caused great conceptual difficulties.

The long history of Atomism has been marked by the peculiar contrast between the atomic idea's effectiveness in interpreting natural phenomena and its apparently fundamental logical defects. The development of physics and chemistry gradually produced a vast amount of evidence that, in the description of nature, the atomic concept is as indispensable as space and time. Yet physics and chemistry threw little light on the logical difficulties of the concept of indivisibility in natural science. These difficulties indicated that a logically satisfactory atomic theory cannot be "trivial," but must, if possible at all, be "deep." Only in the present century has the contrast between empirical effectiveness and logical deficiency been decreased.

The subtle character of the question of nature's stability and specificity seems to be the main reason for the remarkable difficulty in finding the proper entrance to physics. In spite of the fertility of the Atomist's doctrine, thinkers continued to look for alternatives. Several approaches were developed, including the Aristotelian, which presented a radically different answer to the problem of permanence and change and came to dominate human thinking for almost two thousand years. It was not until the Scientific Revolution in the sixteenth and seventeenth centuries that the Aristotelian scheme was abandoned. Physics obtained a new conceptual framework, and the view of nature again came close to that of the ancient Atomists. In fact, Atomism's revival played an important role in the conceptual transformation leading to reestablishment of a mechanical philosophy.[1]

In providing an exact and deterministic account of the motion of bodies under the influence of forces, the new science of mechanics gave an impressive demonstration of the power of the mathematical approach to the description of nature. Yet mechanics was remarkably powerless in the question of nature's stability and specificity. Although most mechanical philosophers accepted some kind of atomism, the mechanical framework itself contained none. Newton has given a lucid description of his view of the atomic problem against the background of mechanics: ". . . it seems probable to me, that God in the Beginning form'd Matter in solid, massy, hard, impenetrable, moveable Particles, of such Sizes and Figures, and with such other Properties, and in such Proportion to Space, as most conduced to the End for which he form'd them; and that these primitive Particles being Solids, are incomparably harder than any porous Bodies compounded of them; even so very hard, as never to wear or break in

[1] For the history of this phase of Atomism, see, for example, K. Lasswitz, *Geschichte der Atomistik vom Mittelalter bis Newton I-III*, Hamburg, 1890; F. A. Lange, *History of Materialism*, New York 1957; Marie Boas, "The Establishment of the Mechanical Philosophy," *Osiris* **10**, 412 (1952).

[67]

pieces; no ordinary Power being able to divide what God himself made one in the first Creation."[1] Here God plays the role of a chooser of logically arbitrary mechanical parameters. The "why" of the choice is not to be found in the framework of mechanics but in "the End for which he form'd them." The parameters are essential for determining the mechanical course of phenomena, but mechanics gives us no clues as to why they are as they are. Mechanics takes advantage of the stability and specificity of nature, but it does not contain "sufficient reasons" for it.

Further development of physics in the eighteenth and nineteenth centuries brought more and more aspects of phenomena within the reach of mathematical methods. The question of stability and specificity, however, was not essentially altered. The properties of physical objects were characterized by parameters, so-called material constants such as compressibility, viscosity, specific heat, refractive index and dielectric constant. Their meaning was defined by the theory, but their "actual" values could not be derived from the differential laws. The values and the relations between them had to be found by experiment.

At the same time, Atomism was further transformed from a speculative scheme to an empirical science.[2] The study of the simple weight and volume relations in chemical combinations led to the development of the atomic-molecular theory that became the backbone of chemistry.

[1] *Opticks*, Book 3, Part I, Query 31.

[2] For the history of this phase of Atomism, see, for example, Leonard K. Nash, "The Atomic-Molecular Theory," *Harvard Case Histories in Experimental Science*, Case 4, Cambridge, Mass., 1950; I. C. Gregory, *A Short History of Atomism*, London, 1931; A. G. van Melsen, *From Atomos to Atom*, New York, 1960.

Investigation of gases gave another great advance: the kinetic theory of heat which interprets thermal phenomena in terms of irregular molecular motions. The conceptual frameworks of mechanics and thermodynamics are connected through the notion of probability. The thermodynamical concepts are encompassed in a statistical mechanical description. For example, temperature is defined as a statistical parameter.

In the new climate of scientific research, growing recognition of the fertility of Atomism brought to the foreground a question that does not seem to have troubled the Ancients. Was the atomic idea more than a means to "save" the phenomena? Did the world contain atoms in an ontological sense, or were atoms only figments of the imagination? The hypothetical character of atoms remained an issue up to the beginning of the present century.

The increasing importance of the atomic concept also revived the old paradox of indivisible bodies that had parts in a geometrical sense. As in Ancient Atomism, this paradox was usually answered by insisting that although atoms are divisible for the mind they cannot be divided by natural agents. We cannot cut an atom in two, but that is because of limitations of our tools. Had we been restricted only by logic we should have been able to actually dissect the objects that we call atomic.

The development of dynamics and later of hydrodynamics and electrodynamics led to the construction of a variety of models of atoms. In corpuscular philosophy the ultimate units were pictured as solid indestructible pieces of matter. When physics was dominated by the concept of central forces, atoms were often envisaged as pure force-atoms, and their interactions were described in terms of distance-dependent attraction and repulsion.

After the discovery of the elementary laws of fluid mechanics, atoms were sometimes conceived as vortices in a perfect fluid. The study of electrical phenomena gave rise to the view that electricity as well as mass is atomized and that the world of atoms is governed by electromagnetic forces.

The empirical stage of Atomism in physics culminated at the beginning of this century when some of the elementary constituents of matter were identified by experiment, and the nuclear model of the atom was established.[1] It was found that matter is built of a few kinds of components. A chemical atom is not a single particle, but a composite system of elementary particles. According to the Rutherford nuclear model, an atom consists of a positively charged central part or nucleus that is very small compared to the size of the atom but contains almost all of its mass, and a number of relatively light negatively charged electrons bound to the nucleus by electrostatic attraction.

Mechanical and electrodynamical ideas proved their large scope when they made it possible to identify the building blocks of matter and to specify their mass and charge. It is true that the building blocks are not, as Democritus held, distinguished primarily by their geometrical shape. But Democritus was correct in maintaining that the ultimate constituents of matter have attributes that are expressible in the language we use to describe physical phenomena on the ordinary scale. The elementary particles are inert and electrical.

---

[1] The development of atomic models, especially the Rutherford atom, has been described by J. L. Heilbron in his Ph.D. dissertation, University of California, Berkeley, 1964 (to be published).

The nuclear model gave atomic physics a solid basis, and its remarkable simplicity seemed to open great new prospects for Democritus' program of anchoring the physical and chemical properties of substances in the attributes of the atomic constituents. Thus the model suggested a distinction between properties determined by the configuration of the electrons around the nucleus, and properties dependent on the internal constitution of the nucleus. That the nucleus itself is a composite system is evidenced by such phenomena as radioactivity. All the ordinary physical and chemical properties of matter, except mass, are determined by the electronic part of the atom, and because of the relatively small size and large mass of the nucleus, the configuration of the electrons could be expected to depend primarily on one quantity only, namely the nuclear charge. This indicated that the position of a chemical element in Mendeleev's periodic table, its atomic number, was given by the number of elementary electric charges on its nucleus.

However, a closer study of the nuclear model soon revived the logical difficulties of atomic theory. Further progress seemed to be impossible without at least a partial solution of these difficulties. On account of the composite character of atoms the problem now had two parts: (1) why are there elementary particles and why do they have just those charges and masses measured? (2) why do atomic systems composed of electrons and nuclei have stability and specific properties? It turned out that these two parts of the atomic problem could be treated separately. The first is still unsolved. No key has yet been found to the ancient Atomists' idea that there is a limit to the divisibility of matter.

Quantum mechanics has provided the solution to the

second part of the problem. The character of this solution shows that the Greek Atomists seized upon something very fundamental when they introduced the concept of indivisibility into the description of nature. The problem of atomic stability and specificity was not solved by the discovery of a new type of force regulating the motion of the electrons around the nucleus. It was solved by the discovery that the agency which prevents a chemical atom from collapsing and endows it with characteristic properties is a new feature of atomicity. Thus, the old question of nature's specific forms was seen to have more than one root. There is in nature a stabilizing agency distinct from that which manifests itself in the existence of the elementary particles of matter. This agency is called the quantum of action.

III

Quantum mechanics is the theory of the quantum of action. It forms a new chapter in the history of Atomism in two respects. First, it deals with a new type of atomicity. The idea of the atomicity of matter is among the oldest in the description of nature, but the atomicity embodied in the quantum was completely outside the intellectual horizon until this century. Secondly, quantum physics is not merely a set of experimentally established relationships; its core is a mathematically coherent and consistent formalism containing the quantum as the characteristic element. Thus, with the development of quantum mechanics atomic science is no longer purely empirical. The basis has been laid for studying the logic of the concept of atomicity as applied in the description of nature. This basis is of course limited since quantum mechanics presents only a partial solution of the atomic problem. Further illumination of this problem would be provided by a theory containing the clue to the individuality of elementary particles and to the logical relation between this individuality and the quantum of action.

The quantum constant had actually been discovered about a decade before the broad aspects of atomic constitution were clarified. Its discovery did not come from the line of research that led to the nuclear model, but from the study of the statistical aspects of electromagnetic radiation. In 1900 Planck realized that the empirically established relation between energy and frequency of thermal radiation at a given temperature could be obtained by introducing a new universal constant into the statistical theory.[1] This constant had the physical dimension of an "action" (length × momentum or time × energy), and Planck called it the elementary quantum of action.

The brief period of less than three decades when quantum mechanics was created is one of the most interesting in the development of physics.[2] It was a time of

[1] For the development leading to Planck's discovery, see M. Planck, "Zur Geschichte der Auffindung des physikalischen Wirkungsquantums," *Die Naturwissenschaften* **31**, 153 (1943); L. Rosenfeld, "La première phase de l'évolution de la Theorie des Quanta," *Osiris* **2**, 149 (1936); M. J. Klein, "Max Planck and the Beginnings of the Quantum Theory," *Arch. His. Exact Sci.* **1**, 459 (1962); M. J. Klein, "Planck, Entropy and Quanta, 1901–1906," *The Natural Philosopher* **1**, (1936); E. Whittaker, *A History of the Theories of Aether and Electricity*, New York, 1960, Vol. II, Ch. III.

[2] There is as yet no comprehensive treatise of the history of quantum physics. Valuable information may be found in: "Die ersten Jahre der Theorie von Niels Bohr uber den Bau der Atome," *Die Naturwissenschaften* **11**, 533–624 (1923); A. Rubinowicz, "Ursprung und Entwicklung der älteren Quantentheorie," *Handbuch der Physik*, 2. Auflage, Vol. XXIV[1], Ch. I; E. Whittaker, *op. cit.*, Ch. III, IV, VIII and IX; S. Tomonaga, *Quantum Mechanics*, Vol. I, Amsterdam, 1962; N. Bohr, Faraday Lecture, *Journ. Chem. Soc.* 349 (1932); N. Bohr, Rutherford Memorial Lecture 1958, *Proc. Phys. Soc.* **78**, 1083 (1961); P. A. Schilpp (ed.), *Albert Einstein. Philosopher-Scientist*, New York, 1949; W. Pauli (ed.), *Niels Bohr and the Development of Physics*, New York and London, 1955; M. Fierz and V. F. Weisskopf (eds.), *Theoretical Physics in the Twentieth century. A memorial volume to Wolfgang Pauli*; F. Bopp (ed.), *Werner Heisenberg und die Physik unserer Zeit*, Braunschweig, 1961; M. J. Klein, "Einstein's First Paper on Quanta," *The Natural Philosopher* **2**, 59 (1963); M. J. Klein, "Einstein and the

profound intellectual transformation, perhaps comparable in some respects to the crisis caused ancient mathematics by the discovery of incommensurable quantities. The atomicity of action presented physicists with a situation that was not only totally unexpected but apparently in direct violation of some of the most well-established scientific principles. Clarifying this situation demanded a thorough revision of the foundations of physical description and led to a new attitude to the nature of physics.

The development of quantum physics divides roughly into two phases. The first ended in 1925–26 with the creation of the quantal formalism. The quantum's early discovery gave the development direction at an early stage, yet the genesis of the formalism was a very complicated process. Here only some of the main points will be discussed. The second phase, particularly relevant for our topic, centered on clarifying the physical meaning of the quantal formalism. This, too, was a complex process, stimulated by interplay between different and often conflicting points of view.

Remarkably, two very dissimilar versions of the formalism, matrix and wave mechanics, were developed almost simultaneously along independent lines of research. The two developments gave rise to different attitudes to the nature of the quantum problem. Even though the mathematical equivalence of the algorithms was soon realized, the differences in their genesis had a

Wave-Particle Duality," *The Natural Philosopher* **3**, (1964); M. Born, *Vorlesungen uber Atommechanik*, Berlin, 1925; M. Born and P. Jordan, *Elementare Quantenmechanik*, Berlin, 1930; M. Born, *Physik im Wandel meiner Zeit*, Braunschweig, 1957; K. Meyer-Abich, *Korrespondenz, Individualität und Komplementariät*, Wiesbaden, 1965.

strong and constructive influence on the discussion of their physical meaning.

The fundamental significance of Planck's discovery was not seen immediately. However, further analysis of the problem of "black-body" radiation made it increasingly certain that the correct radiation law could not come from ordinary physical principles. Indeed, according to the law implied by these principles, the so-called Rayleigh-Jeans law, there could be no thermal equilibrium in a cavity. But while the problem of heat radiation was suited to bring out clearly the breakdown of the classical physical scheme and to identify the missing element, it did not help much to integrate the quantum into a coherent conceptual framework. The impressive coherence and apparent completeness of ordinary electrodynamics indicated that the task of developing a theory of the quantum raised fundamental issues about the nature and scope of physical description.

Application of the quantum idea to the problem of atomic constitution is characteristic of the line of research that led to matrix mechanics. It is a remarkable historical coincidence that the quantum was discovered at about the same time that the basic design of the atom was clarified. This coincidence gave a somewhat indirect and cumbersome entrance to quantum physics, yet it was well suited to bring into focus some of the fundamental aspects of the topic, especially the relation between quantum mechanics and classical mechanics. The attitude that came to dominate discussion of the quantal formalism's physical meaning had been fostered during the development of the quantum theory of atomic constitution.

Bohr brought the quantum to bear on the difficulties afflicting the nuclear model of the atom: "Early in my

[76]

stay in Manchester in the spring of 1912 I became convinced that the electronic constitution of the Rutherford atom was governed throughout by the quantum of action."[1] If it is the quantum that stabilizes the nuclear atom and endows it with specific properties, then a detailed study of these properties might furnish a theory of the quantum of action. The line spectra provide the most quantitative expression of the specificity of chemical elements. Since these spectra originate from the atomic electrons, it was surmised that the quantum theory is, so to say, encoded in the spectra and could be found if one succeeded in deciphering the spectral code.

The general features of the quantum-control of the nuclear atom were specified by Bohr in two fundamental postulates.[2] First, an atomic system can exist permanently only in certain so-called stationary states. Each of these states has a well-defined energy, and they form a discrete set. Any change of the energy of the system amounts to a "complete transition" between two stationary states. The second postulate, the so-called frequency condition, asserts that the radiation emitted or absorbed in such a transition is monochromatic, *i.e.* consists of a pure harmonic wave, with a frequency equal to the energy difference between the two states divided by the quantum. Obviously, these postulates conflict with classical electrodynamics. They were suggested by Planck's quantum description of the harmonic oscillator and by the empirically established spectral regularities.

[1] Rutherford Memorial Lecture, *Proc. Phys. Soc.* **78**, 1083 (1961), p. 1086.
[2] Bohr's classic papers of 1913 have been reprinted, with an introduction by L. Rosenfeld, in Niels Bohr, *On the Constitution of Atoms and Molecules*, Copenhagen and New York, 1963.

To connect the postulates with the nuclear atom, Bohr assumed that because the radiative force is small compared with the electrostatic force, classical mechanics is applicable to the motion of the electron in a stationary state. The electronic orbits of the stationary states were selected from the continuous manifold of the mechanically possible orbits by certain "quantum conditions" that were also suggested by Planck's way of fixing the permissible states of an harmonic oscillator.

The two postulates gave the starting point for developing a quantum theory of line spectra. Step by step the description was enriched, and more and more characteristics of the quantum problem emerged as the theory was applied to a growing number of problems. The expansion of the description was especially stimulated by Einstein's introduction in 1916 of probability coefficients to regulate the transition processes, and by the attempts in the early twenties to create a quantum theory of the optical phenomena, such as reflection, absorption and dispersion, that are associated with the passage of light through a material medium. This theory prepared the way for Heisenberg's discovery of matrix mechanics in 1925.

The development during the twelve years between the theory of the hydrogen spectrum and the formulation of matrix mechanics was an intricate process that has not yet been analyzed in detail. It is difficult to trace how the general way of thinking about the quantum problem evolved. From the beginning, the leading view seems to have been that the breakdown of ordinary physical principles when applied to such phenomena as thermal radiation and line spectra not only required radically new assumptions, but also gave the freedom to make such assumptions. Apart from mutual consistency, the only guide for formulating the new assumptions was the structure of Planck's theory and the empirically established spectral regularities. It was believed that the quantum theory of the hydrogen spectrum could be gradually extended into a conceptual framework as coherent and complete as ordinary electrodynamics.

Increasingly, the logical relation between quantum theory and classical theory became a critical issue. Important features of this relation had already come to light in Planck's work. Although his radiation law required non-classical assumptions for its derivation, it was not totally unconnected with classical physics. For large wavelengths and high temperatures its predictions coincided with those of ordinary statistical electrodynamics. One of the most striking aspects of Bohr's theory of the hydrogen atom was the lack of any direct connection between the kinematics of the electron and the frequency of the emitted light. Bohr showed that the usual connection between spectrum and motion reappeared in the domain of large quantum numbers, where his theory predicts radiation of the same frequencies as those predicted by classical electron theory. Einstein's introduction of probability coefficients suggested that this agreement in the limit be extended to include intensities of the emitted light.

A closer study of the asymptotic coincidence of the predictions of classical and quantum theory put Bohr on the track of a peculiar "formal analogy" between the two theories. This analogy was expressed in the correspondence principle which states that to each of the quantum transitions there corresponds a certain Fourier component of the classical motion of the electron, and that for large quantum numbers the emitted light is identical with that

[79]

emitted classically by the corresponding Fourier component. The correspondence principle became a powerful tool for extending the scope of the theory of line spectra, and the question of its deeper meaning gradually became dominant.

In its original form the correspondence principle could be considered a generalization of a particular feature of classical electron theory, namely the connection between the composition of the light emitted and the orbital motion of the emitting charge. As the quantum theory of line spectra was applied to a wide range of problems, it was increasingly apparent that the formal analogy between classical and quantum theory was very close and of fundamental significance. The success of "the cycle of ideas of the Correspondence Principle" suggested that the formal analogy might be the clue to establishing the new algorithm since this analogy might suggest the structure of a quantum mechanics.

Making the correspondence principle the main tool for constructing a quantal formalism was presumably the most important step in preparing matrix mechanics. It produced an attitude to the quantum problem (often called the "Kopenhagener Geist der Quantentheorie") which "has directed the entire development of modern atomic physics."[1] In the early twenties the characteristics of this attitude were still rather obscure, but they became much more articulated during the following decade.[2]

[1] W. Heisenberg, *The Physical Principles of the Quantum Theory*, Chicago, 1930. Preface.

[2] The history of the correspondence attitude to the quantum problem is still very little explored. The published papers apparently are not sufficient source material for describing this

[80]

Tomonaga[1] has given a good description of this crucial turn in the quantum development. As he points out, the correspondence procedure could not be considered fundamentally significant when judged by ordinary principles of natural philosophy. In the correspondence procedure a physical problem is first treated in terms of classical ideas. The results are then "reinterpreted" by replacing certain classical quantities with their corresponding quantum concepts. For example, the classical frequency of the electron's orbital motion is replaced by the quantum frequency of the corresponding transition between stationary states; the square of the Fourier component of the dipole moment is replaced by the corresponding transition probability. The correspondence procedure seems to be no more than a convenient recipe for determining quantum mechanical quantities, a useful calculation device that supplements Bohr's theory of line spectra. It is natural to anticipate that "when we arrive at the true theory, the first thing to be clarified is the mechanism through which only a certain discrete set of states can occur in nature and then to understand what determines why some atoms jump from A to B at time T_B while some others jump from A to B' at $t_{B'}$ and so on. We would then

---

development. Much valuable information may be found in: N. Bohr, "The Quantum Theory of Line Spectra," *D. Kgl. Danske Vidensk. Selsk. Skrifter* 8 Raekke, IV, 1, Parts I–III, Copenhagen, 1918–22; N. Bohr, "On the Application of the Quantum Theory to Atomic Structure," *Proceedings of the Cambridge Philosophical Society* (supplement), Cambridge, 1924. See also the articles by Leon Rosenfeld and Erik Rüdinger, and by Werner Heisenberg in S. Rosenthal (ed.), *Niels Bohr*, Amsterdam 1967; and the works by Rubinowicz and Meyer-Abich referred to in footnote 2 on page 74.

[1] *Quantum Mechanics*, Vol. I, pp. 159f.

be able to calculate the frequency of occurrences of such transitions and presumably would find that it actually is in harmony with the correspondence principle result in the limit of large [quantum numbers]."[1]

In contrast to this view of the future theory, the Copenhagen group of physicists "began to think differently. Namely, they began to realize that the nature of the discontinuities or of the transitions should be sought in the correspondence principle itself and that there are no *ad hoc* fundamental laws which have no correspondence to the classical theory. According to the viewpoint of common sense, a hidden mechanism is to exist to make the states discontinuous, and there should be laws of a more fundamental nature which describe the course of a transition, but this viewpoint should be abandoned."[2] According to the new view of the quantum problem, "it is anticipated that the correct laws of the quantum world should be obtained not by introducing certain additional laws for the transition mechanism but instead by a revised form, expressed mathematically in a clear-cut way, of the correspondence principle itself."[3]

In the true theory one will not have to first treat a problem classically and then reinterpret the result quantum mechanically. The true theory "must be expressed, from the very beginning, in terms of only quantum mechanical quantities obeying certain laws. These laws will be similar in form to those of classical mechanics, or electrodynamics, governing the corresponding classical quantities and in the limit of very large quantum numbers the conclusions of the two will coincide with each other."[4]

On the correspondence approach to the quantum theory,

---

[1] *Op. cit.*, p. 159.   [2] *Op. cit.*, pp. 159f.
[3] *Op. cit.*, p. 160.   [4] *Ibid.*

one should not look for a mechanism to explain the fact that in the quantum domain a periodic dynamical system has a discrete set of stationary states. Rather, one should consider this discontinuity as the quantum analog of the classical fact that the motion of a periodic system contains a fundamental mode and a discrete set of higher harmonics. Similarly, one should not look for a mechanism to account for the discontinuous quantum transitions. "What the correspondence principle tells us is that the jump is due to the interaction between the atom and radiation, corresponding to the classical fact that the orbit of the electron shrinks more and more by emitting light due to this interaction, and that each transition corresponds to a Fourier component of the classical orbital motion, the probability of the transition being given by something which corresponds to the square of the Fourier amplitude. There is no mechanism for the transition process, independent of the shrinking of orbital motion presupposed in the structure of the correspondence principle."[1]

Tomonaga adds some remarks about how one may in the early twenties have anticipated more specifically the structure of the quantal description. These remarks are perhaps too articulated to be historically correct, but they illuminate the correspondence way of thinking. The formal analogy between the classical and quantal description of the nuclear atom indicated that "an important role would be played in the true theory by a certain quantity which, when squared, determines the probability of the transition and would take over the concept of the orbital motion in conventional mechanics. Furthermore, this quantity in the true theory would oscillate with the quantum theoretically correct frequency instead of the classical one v_τ.

[1] *Op. cit.*, p. 161.

[83]

Thus this "certain quantity," describing the statistical properties of the atom, would play in the true theory a fundamental role similar to that of the orbital motion in the classical theory. What we have called the "motion" in the classical sense would fade away in the new theory and the time variation of this "certain quantity" which gives rise to the statistical nature of various transitions would constitute the main subject of the theory. Corresponding to the circumstance in the classical theory that the emission of light is due to the interaction between the orbital motion of the electrons and the electromagnetic field, the transition would then be caused by the interaction between the "certain quantity" and the electromagnetic field. The temporal variation of this "certain quantity" would be determined in the same way as the Fourier component of the orbital motion in the classical theory, although the causal description of the transition itself would have to be given up. Thus the transition law in the new theory would not be obtained by introducing an additional mechanical entity into the classical theory and giving a new law to govern it, but instead, would be achieved without increasing the number of basic elements of the theory."[1]

In the summer of 1925 Heisenberg discovered the structure of the quantal algorithm.[2] His reasoning was based on two general ideas. One derived from the way he conceived of the difficulties in the previous quantum

[1] *Ibid.*
[2] "Über quantentheoretische Umdeutung kinematischer und mechanischer Beziehungen," *Zeitschrift für Physik* 33, 879 (1925). Reprinted in M. Born, W. Heisenberg and P. Jordan, "Zur Begründung der Matrizenmechanik," *Dokumente der Naturwissenschaft, Abteilung Physik*, Band II, Stuttgart, 1962.

theory. He thought the root of these difficulties was that the formal rules in the theory of line spectra contained quantities unobservable not only in practice but possibly also in principle. As examples of such quantities he mentioned the position and time of revolution of the electron that are used to calculate observables like the energy of the hydrogen atom. The hope that current unobservables might eventually become experimentally accessible would be justified only if the quantum rules were "in themselves methodologically satisfactory and applicable to a clearly delimited domain of quantum problems" ("in sich konsequent und auf einen bestimmt umgrenzten Bereich quantentheoretischer Probleme anvendbar").[1] However, the rules necessitate using classical mechanics, yet at the same time contain completely non-classical elements like the frequency condition; and there is no criterion that makes it possible to say in general when they hold and when they break down. Thus, it is reasonable to abandon hope of observing the quantities in question and to try instead to formulate a new set of quantum relationships that contain only observable quantities.

Heisenberg's suggestion that the search for a satisfactory quantum algorithm should be based on the requirement that all quantities entering a physical description must be observable in principle was of course inspired by Einstein's analysis of simultaneity. In emphasizing a profound similarity between the problems posed by the finite propagation of all actions and the limited divisibility of all actions, Heisenberg brought into the foreground the epistemological aspects of the quantum issue.

The other general idea that played an important role in Heisenberg's considerations was the correspondence

[1] *Op. cit.*, p. 879.

principle. During the early twenties the content of this principle had been considerably broadened. The quantum theory of dispersion suggested that the "formal analogy" went much beyond a "correspondence" between quantum transition processes and classical Fourier components of the orbital motion. It seemed as if there would be a striking similarity between a fully developed quantum theory and the classical theory. Thus Heisenberg was able to add an important specification to his program of establishing a quantum algorithm of relations between observable quantities: this algorithm was to be as closely analogous to classical mechanics as possible.

Guided by the observability dictum whose meaning was considered well understood, and the correspondence principle whose epistemological significance was still obscure, Heisenberg went on to develop the basic features of the new mathematical structure. As indicated by the title of his paper, "Über quantentheoretische Umdeutung kinematischer und mechanischer Beziehungen," he proceeded in two stages. He first considered the question of how to determine the quantity which in the quantum algorithm is to correspond to or represent the classical position variable $x(t)$. Presumably it was impossible to ascribe to an electron a position in space as a function of time in terms of observable quantities. However, the question could be answered by recognizing that in quantum theory as well as in classical theory, emitted radiation describable in terms of frequency, amplitude, polarization and phase can be associated with an electron. These quantities are subjected to different rules of composition in the two theories: for example, the quantum rule for the composition of frequencies is identical with the Rydberg–Ritz combination principle. Furthermore, in classical

[86]

theory the spectrum of the emitted radiation completely reflects the kinematics of the electron. The correspondence view made it natural to assume that the quantum analog of a kinematical quantity like $x(t)$ could be determined from the Fourier expression of the classical motion. The fact that in quantum theory the frequency of the radiation accompanying a transition process depends on both the initial and the final stationary state prevented a "direct translation" of the classical Fourier sum and indicated that the quantum representative of $x(t)$ should be an array of elements each dependent on two integers and each corresponding to an element in the Fourier expression.

Heisenberg next considered the question of how the ordinary arithmetical operations should be performed with the new symbols. Addition presented no problem, and he found the rule for multiplication from the quantum composition law of frequencies. To his great surprise, it turned out that the product of representatives corresponding to two classical physical quantities would not, in general, be equal to the product of the same representatives with the order of the factors reversed. In other words, quantum multiplication is not commutative.

Turning now to the reinterpretation of mechanical relationships, Heisenberg made an exceedingly daring and ingenious use of the correspondence idea. He proposed that his quantum symbols, even though they apparently could not be given a geometrical interpretation, should be subjected to laws of motion, and that these laws should be completely similar to the laws of motion in classical physics. In this way, his scheme became a coherent physical theory. By treating a few simple examples he was able to illustrate the workings of the new methods.

The mathematical structure of quantum mechanics was soon developed further.[1] It was shown that the quantal formalism was a mathematical generalization of classical Hamiltonian mechanics. The quantum representatives of the classical physical variables were found to be Hermitean matrices. The time-evolution of these matrices is governed by equations of motion of a Hamiltonian form. The solution of these equations was seen to be equivalent to an eigenvalue problem; a transformation to the principal axes of a Hermitean matrix. The formalism contains commutation rules specifying how two oppositely ordered products of canonically conjugate matrices are related. These rules, which take over the role of the old "quantum conditions," are the only expressions containing the quantum.

The discovery of matrix mechanics clarified the mathematical meaning of that formal analogy between classical and quantum theory which had given rise to the correspondence idea. Now it could be seen that the formal analogy had signified that the quantal formalism should emerge as a mathematical generalization of classical mechanics. In fact, the structure of the new formalism was as similar to that of Hamiltonian mechanics as was consistent with the basic quantum postulates which, contrary to their status in Bohr's theory, form an organic part of quantum mechanics. "Dieser Ähnlichkeit der neuen Theorie mit der klassischen entspricht es auch, dass von einem selbständigen Korrespondenzprinzip neben dieser Theorie wohl nicht die Rede sein kann; vielmehr kann die Theorie selbst als exakte Formulierung des Bohrschen Korrespondenzgedankens aufgefasst werden. Es wird eine wichtige Aufgabe für die weitere En-

[1] Especially by Born, Jordan, Heisenberg and Dirac.

[88]

twicklung der Theorie sein, die Art dieser Korrespondenz genauer zu untersuchen und der Übergang von der symbolischen Quantengeometrie in die anschauliche klassiche Geometrie zu beschreiben."[1]

The second route to the quantum formalism, that which led to wave mechanics, will be only briefly indicated here.[2] It was opened by Einstein's work in 1905 on the nature of radiation. In this work the new element of atomicity entered as the hypothesis of light quanta, *i.e.* the assumption that electromagnetic radiation in free space is propagated in the form of individual energy quanta each occupying a minute region of space. It was the study of fluctuation phenomena in cavity radiation that suggested the idea of corpuscles of light. As is well known, fluctuation phenomena in gases and liquids, *e.g.* Brownian motion, had similarly given strong support to the idea of the atomic constitution of matter.

The light quantum hypothesis immediately offered a "heuristic" explanation of a number of phenomena that were as inexplicable on the basis of the ordinary electromagnetic theory of light as was the spectral distribution in cavity radiation. It indicated that the question of the nature of light had after all not been settled definitely, and that a core of truth remained in the old corpuscular theory. It suggested the program of developing a theory of radiation in which both wave and particle features were incorporated. The fact that the frequency concept occurred in the very definition of a light quantum articulated the paradoxical character of the hypothesis in a way

[1] M. Born, W. Heisenberg and P. Jordan, "Zur Quantenmechanik II," *Zeitschrift für Physik* 35, 557 (1962), p. 558.

[2] For this development, see especially the two papers by M. J. Klein referred to in footnote 2 on page 74.

reminiscent of the old logical difficulties in atomic physics.

It took a long time for the light quantum hypothesis to be generally accepted; its unavoidability was gradually demonstrated by experimental evidence. In 1924 de Broglie proposed the bold idea that a similar wave-particle duality holds for material particles. In searching for the equation governing the "matter waves" corresponding to particles acted upon by forces, Schrödinger was guided by the analogy between optics and mechanics. In terms of this analogy Schrödinger's wave mechanics, discovered in 1926, is related to ordinary mechanics in a way similar to the way wave optics is related to geometrical optics. Ordinary mechanics emerges as a special case of a more general theory. Its special feature, the idea of well-defined orbits, is an approximation equivalent to the idea of rays in geometrical optics. On this approach, the quantum is viewed as an element of a wave theory of matter. A typical quantum mechanical problem consists in seeking the eigen-solutions of a linear differential equation, the Schrödinger equation, with given boundary conditions.

The quantum formalism demonstrated that a logically consistent atomic theory is possible, and it brought Democritus' program for the description of nature within the reach of mathematical methods. On the basis of quantum mechanics it is possible to explain and predict the properties of systems that are composed of atomic nuclei and electrons. Modern atomic physics has thus given great impetus to many sciences that deal with the properties, reactions and evolution of matter, such as chemistry, astronomy and biology.

With the formalism established, the study of the quantum problem entered a new phase. Both versions of the formalism employ mathematical methods created long ago, and mathematicians were well acquainted with the equivalence between the matrix and the wave formulation of these methods. From being "encoded" in the regularities of line spectra, quantum theory had been translated into a mathematical structure whose elements could be manipulated according to well-defined rules. But this was not thought to be a full solution of the quantum problem. The analysis had to be carried a further step in which quantum theory was to be translated from the mathematical scheme into the language of the physicists. This step is often referred to as the physical interpretation of the mathematical formalism.

Unlike the analysis of the foundations of special relativity, the discussion of the physical interpretation of quantum mechanics still continues and has gone through several phases. No general agreement has been reached, and the topic may still be insufficiently explored. The view that has long been most widely accepted although challenged by many eminent physicists is often called the Copenhagen interpretation.[1] Its bases were laid in

[1] So far no comprehensive account of the Copenhagen interpretation has been published. The following references are particularly instructive: N. Bohr, "The Quantum Postulate and the Recent Development of Atomic Theory," *Nature* **121**, 580 (1928) (reprinted in *Atomic Theory and the Description of Nature*, Cambridge, 1961); N. Bohr, "Chemistry and the Quantum Theory of Atomic Constitution" (Faraday Lecture), *Journal of the Chemical Society*, February, 1932, p. 349; N. Bohr and L. Rosenfeld, "Zur Frage der Messbarkeit der elektromagnetischen Feldgrössen," *Det kgl. Danske Videnskabernes Selskab. Matematisk-fysiske Meddelelser* XII, 8, Copenhagen, 1933; N. Bohr, "Can Quantum Mechanical Description of Physical Reality be Considered Complete?" *Phys. Rev.* **48**, 696 (1935); N. Bohr, "The Causality Problem

two classic papers by Heisenberg and Bohr from the late twenties, and it was later developed through discussions especially between Bohr and Einstein. It was thoroughly tested and much advanced in Bohr and Rosenfeld's investigation of the measurability of field quantities. The following will trace some of the key points in Bohr's and Heisenberg's views on the nature of the quantum problem. It is assumed that these views, though still needing further clarification, contain the deepest insight into the quantum problem obtained thus far.

There were several indications that the task of understanding the quantum was not completed by the creation of the quantal formalism. First, the physical significance

in Atomic Physics," *New Theories in Physics* (Report on Warsaw conference May 30th–June 3rd, 1938), Paris, 1939, p. 11; N. Bohr, "On the Notions of Causality and Complementarity," *Dialectica* 2, 312 (1948); N. Bohr, "Discussion with Einstein on Epistemological Problems in Atomic Physics," *Albert Einstein, Philosopher-Scientist* (P. A. Schilpp, ed.), p. 199, Evanston, 1949 (reprinted in *Atomic Physics and Human Knowledge*, New York, 1958); N. Bohr, "Quantum Physics and Philosophy—Causality and Complementarity," *Philosophy in the Mid-century* (R. Klibansky, ed.), Florence, 1958 (reprinted in N. Bohr, *Last Essays* New York, 1964); W. Heisenberg, "Über den auschanlichen Inhalt der quanten- theoretischen Kinematik und Mechanik," *Zeitschrift für Physik* 43, 172 (1927); W. Heisenberg, *The Physical Principles of Quantum Theory*, Chicago, 1930; W. Heisenberg, "50 Jahre Quantentheorie," *Die Naturwissenschaften* 38, 49 (1951); W. Heisenberg, *Physics and Philosophy*, New York, 1958 (especially Chs. II, III, VIII and X); W. Heisenberg: "Quantum Theory and its Interpretation," *Niels Bohr* (S. Rosenthal, ed.), p. 94, Amsterdam, 1967; K. Meyer-Abich, *Korrespondenz, Individualität, Komplementarität*, Wiesbaden, 1965; Max Born, "Zur Statistischen Deutung der Quantentheorie," *Dokumente der Naturwissenschaft, Abteilung_Physik*, Band I, Stuttgart, 1962.

of some of the formalism's peculiar relationships, like the rules of quantum mechanical multiplication, was far from clear. These abstract relationships presumably reflected profound aspects of nature which might also be expressible in physical terms. Secondly, although the formalism was readily applicable to some physical problems such as calculating energy levels of the harmonic oscillator and the hydrogen atom, in other cases it was hard to extract physically relevant information. Some physical or "intuitive" point of view was needed to apply the formalism and to suggest qualitative answers to simple physical questions. In particular, the mathematical structure of the formalism gave no immediate clues to clarifying the paradoxes that had long typified quantum physics. They pertained especially to two questions: the nature of radiation and matter, and the meaning of "complete transitions between stationary states" or "quantum jumps." These paradoxes indicated the logical subtlety of the whole issue and suggested that fundamental principles of the description of nature were involved.

A third factor motivated analysis of the interpretation question. The different routes along which the two versions of the formalism were developed had given rise to diverging attitudes to the quantum problem. Further, matrix and wave mechanics suggested quite different views regarding the physical content of the quantum formalism. Thus at a time when there could be little doubt about the correct mathematical theory of the quantum, a controversy arose about the nature of the quantum problem. Heisenberg and Bohr's initial investigations were stimulated by Schrödinger.[1] He tried to show that his wave mechanics restores the validity of the old dictum

[1] *Die Naturwissenschaften* **14**, 664 (1926).

that nature does not make jumps, *i.e.* that in his formulation the quantum problem does not necessitate a break with the ordinary description of a physical phenomenon as a continuous deterministic chain of events in space and time. Similarly, the later discussion was largely generated by Einstein's efforts[1] to prove by concrete examples that quantum mechanics does not give a complete account of the physics of a quantum system, that it does not refer to all elements of physical reality in the quantum domain. Again, Bohr and Rosenfeld's investigation[2] of measurement problems in quantum electrodynamics was a response to Landau and Peierls' study[3] concluding that in this area there is a discrepancy between the formalism and the physically available measuring procedures that makes the field concept inapplicable in quantum theory.

As in the development of the formalism itself, the entrance to the study of the interpretation question was traced by means of a few general ideas. Essentially, these

[1] See Bohr's article "Discussion with Einstein on Epistemological Problems in Atomic Physics," and Einstein's "Remarks to the Essays Appearing in this Collective Volume," *Albert Einstein, Philosopher-Scientist* (P. A. Schilpp, ed.), Evanston, 1949; A. Einstein, B. Podolsky, N. Rosen, "Can Quantum-mechanical Description of Physical Reality be considered Complete?" *Phys. Rev.* **47**, 777 (1935), and Bohr's answer, *Phys. Rev.* **48**, 696 (1935); A. Einstein, "Physics and Reality," *Journal of the Franklin Institute* **221**, 349 (1936); A. Einstein, "Quantum-Mechanik und Wiklichkeit," *Dialectica* **2**, 320 (1948).

[2] "Zur Frage der Messbarkeit der electromagnetischen Feldgrössen," *Dan. Vid. Selsk. Math.-fys. Medd.* XII, 8 (1933).

[3] "Erweiterung des Unbestimmtheitsprinzips für die relativistische Quantentheorie," *Zeitschrift für Physik* **69**, 56 (1931).

were the ones that had illuminated the mathematical part of the task; the concept of observability and the correspondence argument. Because they had to be sharpened for this new role, their mutual connection and profound epistemological significance began to emerge.

The quantum theorists possessed the proper mathematical formalism but still lacked the physical understanding of the quantum problem, and the question was of course if and how the formalism could show the way to the physical understanding. The treatment of this question, which forms the core of the subsequent discussion, threw much light on the relation between mathematics and physics. Above all, it showed that the relation was still unclear, despite a widespread conviction to the contrary among physicists and philosophers.

The idea of observability went through a significant transformation in the period between Heisenberg's fundamental paper on the quantum formalism and his paper on its physical interpretation.[1] Originally, Heisenberg had considered the observation question separable from and indeed prior to the establishment of the algorithm, but he had not specified the meaning of observability. From the beginning of quantum theory, as in the theory of relativity, imaginary or conceptual experiments had been the main tool in analyzing the foundations. These experiments are not to test the theory in the usual sense of finding how well its predictions fit the empirical data. Instead, the experiments extract the physical meaning of the theory's basic principles. By

[1] Much interesting information about this formative period is contained in Heisenberg's articles in *Die Naturwissenschaften* and *Niels Bohr* (S. Rozental, ed.) referred to in the footnote on p. 92.

applying the theory to situations that manifest these principles in a concise and striking way one tries to force the principles to reveal their physical content. The difficulties of identifying the physical significance of the quantum formalism made it necessary to examine the idea of conceptual experimentation more closely. Heisenberg was convinced that even though it was often difficult to state which answer the formalism would give when applied to a particular imaginary experiment, the formalism nevertheless contained the answer to any legitimate question in the quantum domain. But what did "legitimate" mean in this connection? On one hand the mathematics itself prescribes the rules for formulating its theorems. On the other hand, it is we who ask the physical questions, specify the physical situation or conditions of the conceptual experiment. Whatever the criteria of legitimacy that apply to these questions, they do not seem to be derived from the quantum formalism. One would expect these criteria that determine the meaning of observability to have some other roots, perhaps philosophical. One might also doubt that they exist.

In a recent article,[1] Heisenberg has told that the decisive step in his thinking about the interpretation question was his conjecture that the class of experiments permitted by the quantum formalism is identical with the class of experiments that nature permits in the quantum domain. In particular, the restrictions the formalism imposes on experimentation are also imposed by nature itself. In this view, the mathematical scheme is basic to the physical interpretation in the sense that it provides the criteria of legitimacy for formulating the physical

[1] "Quantum Theory and its Interpretation," *Niels Bohr* (S. Rozental, ed.), p. 94.

questions asked of nature and the answers that can be obtained in experiments. Observability is decided on the basis of the mathematical framework. In the attempts to develop this line of thinking, the correspondence argument about quantum physics' relation to classical physics assumed an increasingly dominant role.

As indicated by the title of his 1927 paper, "Über den anschaulichen Inhalt der quantentheoretischen Kinematik und Mechanik," Heisenberg thought of the interpretation question as a task of providing a visualizable or intuitive understanding of the quantum mechanical relations. He started his discussion with a few remarks about the meaning of such a type of understanding. We have an intuitive understanding of a physical theory when we can imagine its experimental consequences in all simple cases and have convinced ourselves that its application never involves internal contradictions. For example, we understand intuitively Einstein's idea of a closed three-dimensional space because we can consistently represent its experimental consequences. It is true that these consequences contradict our ordinary space–time concepts, but the applicability of accustomed concepts on a cosmological scale can be inferred neither from our laws of thought nor from experience.

Thus, to interpret the quantal formalism is to provide an intuitive understanding of the fundamental quantum mechanical relations. Such an understanding ought to enable us to guess qualitatively the answers that the formalism will give when applied to simple physical situations. It also ought to enable us to clarify the many contradictions and paradoxes that have so far afflicted the topic. The structure of the fundamental commutation relations indicates that when describing quantum phenomena

[97]

we cannot uncritically apply concepts like position, velocity, momentum and energy. The scope of these concepts in the region governed by the quantal formalism has to be ascertained by examination of relevant imaginary experiments.

As Heisenberg showed, this examination gave as a result that each of the elementary concepts which in the classical theory is employed for describing a mechanical system can be applied without any restrictions in the account of quantum systems. For example, the position of an atomic object can be measured with unlimited accuracy by means of a microscope employing radiation of sufficiently short wavelength, a gamma-ray microscope. However, the quantal formalism imposes a characteristic limitation on the combined use of conjugate variables. This reciprocal limitation, known as the indeterminacy or uncertainty relations, proved to be an immediate consequence of the basic commutation rules. The relations state that the product of the lattitudes in fixing a pair of canonically conjugate variables is at least of the order of magnitude of the quantum constant.

Heisenberg illustrated the meaning of the uncertainty relations by applying them to a number of instructive imaginary experiments. For example, in measuring position with a gamma-ray microscope the Compton effect plays an essential role. When the photon on its way from the light source into the microscope is scattered by the atomic object, the momentum of that object undergoes a discontinuous change. This abrupt change of momentum is greater the harder or more short-waved the photon, *i.e.* the more accurate the position measurement. Thus, at the moment when the position of the object is known, its momentum can be known only to an accuracy less than the discontinuous change caused by the Compton recoil. If, conversely, we want to determine the momentum of an object with known mass, we may again use radiation and infer the object's velocity from the Doppler shift of the reflected light. But in order to diminish the object's change of velocity due to the Compton effect, we must in this case use light of long wave length, and so our knowledge of the position of the object will be correspondingly more imprecise.

The reciprocal relation between the accuracy of position and momentum determination gives an intuitive understanding of the quantum mechanical commutation rule for the two variables. Similar restrictions hold for the combined measurements of any other pair of conjugate variables such as time and energy, or angle and action variables. All experiments, imaginary as well as actual, that can be made in the quantum region are subjected to the limitations stated in the uncertainty relations.

Having thus shown that as far as their physical meaning is concerned the commutation rules are symbolic expressions of the quantum-imposed restrictions on measurements, Heisenberg went on to argue that it is these observational restrictions themselves that provide room for all the peculiar relationships in quantum physics. To explain this remarkable way of extracting positive implications from negative statements, he again compared the situation in quantum physics with that in the theory of special relativity. The notion of simultaneity of spatially separated events can be defined only by experimental procedures which involve essentially the propagation velocity of light signals. If it were possible to give a "sharper" definition of this notion, for example if there existed signals propagating with an infinite velocity, then the theory of relativity would be impossible. Since the very definition of simultaneity in special relativity involves the velocity of light, that theory excludes the existence of such signals. Here, too, there is accordance between what is mathematically permitted by the formalism and what is physically possible in nature. The relativistic definition of simultaneity provides room for the postulate that the velocity of light has the same value for all inertial observers. In other words, it is the occurrence of the characteristic propagation velocity in the very specification of the measuring procedure for the synchronization of spatially separated clocks that makes it possible to avoid the apparent contradiction between the postulate of the constancy of the velocity of light and the unambiguous use of the words position, time and velocity.

In a similar way, the quantum of action plays an essential role in specifying procedures for combined measurements of conjugate physical variables. If a pair of such variables could be given a fixation "sharper" than that permitted by the uncertainty relations, for example if there existed physical actions smaller than Planck's constant, then quantum mechanics would be impossible. It is the lack of possibility of such a fixation that leaves room for the commutation rules, or that permits conjugate variables to be non-commutative and yet retain their ordinary physical meaning. In other words, the fact that observability is more restricted in quantum physics than in classical physics is not just a negative aspect. This loss is exploited in the quantal formalism, just as in relativity, to secure consistency between the non-classical features of the theory and the unambiguous use of the ordinary elementary physical concepts.

Additional insight into the lack of joint observability

[100]

of conjugate physical variables is afforded by visualizing the quantum mechanical representatives of such variables, *i.e.* Hermitean matrices, as tensors in a multi-dimensional space. In this geometrical picture, the non-commutability of two such tensors is reflected in the fact that their principal axes point in different directions. An experimental arrangement specifies a direction in the multi-dimensional space, and obtaining information about a physical variable in such a situation amounts to asking: what is the value of its corresponding matrix or tensor in the given direction? However, this question has a well-defined meaning only if the direction coincides with one of the principal axes of the tensor. If this is not the case, then the matrix possesses no unique value in the given direction, *i.e.* the corresponding physical quantity cannot be sharply fixed by the experimental arrangement in question. Yet, it is still possible to assign a "value with a probable error" to the matrix in the given direction; the probable error depending on the deviation of the direction from a principal axis.

Each experiment in the quantum region thus divides the physical quantities into "known" and "unknown," or into more or less accurately known. One experiment can yield definite predictions about the result of another only if both perform the division into known and unknown in the same way, *i.e.* if they specify the same direction in the abstract space. If they give rise to different divisions, only statistical relationships can connect their results. From the outcome of the first, we can predict only the probabilities of the possible results of the second. Among the wealth of possibilities, the second experiment selects a particular one and thus specifies a new direction and a new set of possibilities and probabilities for further experiments.

One of the most important aspects of the interpretation question is the nature of the connection between the quantum and the classical description, or, as Heisenberg expressed it, the transition from micro to macro mechanics. In the pre-formalism period the study of this problem had given rise to the correspondence argument. More recently the problem had been discussed by Schrödinger[1] in connection with his efforts to show that the wave formulation of the quantal formalism made it possible to avoid the discontinuities or quantum jumps and to return to a continuous space–time description of physical processes. These efforts were based on the view that the wave function represents a real physical field and not a probability amplitude for quantum jumps. On that view, the classical picture of a moving material particle can be approximated to an arbitrary degree by a moving "wave packet," *i.e.* a group of waves that interfere constructively within a small region of space and cancel each other outside. For example, according to the pure wave theory the classical limit of the electronic motion in a hydrogen atom is simply a charged wave packet, built up by superposition of proper vibrations, small compared to the size of the atom and moving around the nucleus in a Kepler orbit.

Against this view, Heisenberg argues that in general the wave group will not stay together but will gradually spread out. In the course of time the electronic wave packet moving around the hydrogen nucleus will fill the whole space in the neighborhood of the nucleus. Only in the case of a harmonic oscillator does the wave packet remain narrow. In Heisenberg's opinion the answer to the question of the emergence of the classical orbit should

[1] *Die Naturwissenschaften* **14**, 664 (1926).

be sought in a completely different direction. If we make a moderately accurate measurement of the position of an electron that was previously known to be in a definite very highly excited state, we will of course loose the exact knowledge of its energy, but we can still determine its momentum within the limits set by the uncertainty relations. The knowledge we have thus acquired about the electron's position and momentum can be represented as a probability packet in ordinary space or in momentum space. After some time a new position measurement is made with the same accuracy as before. But since the packet has spread out, the result of this second measurement can only be predicted statistically. This would also be the case in classical theory where imperfectly known initial conditions make long-term predictions increasingly uncertain. The second measurement selects a subset of the total set of possibilities; it reduces the probability packet to its original size. Then the packet starts spreading out again. One may thus say that the classical orbit emerges only through our observation of it.

At the end of his paper, Heisenberg made some remarks about the roots and implications of the statistical element in the quantal description. He emphasized that this element does not originate from the impossibility of drawing exact conclusions from exactly given data. In all cases where classical physical relations hold between quantities that quantum mechanically are exactly measurable, like the conservation laws of momentum and energy, the same exact relations hold in quantum theory. In the doctrine of causality which states that if we know the present accurately enough we can calculate the future, there is no fault with the conclusion. It is the presupposition that is wrong, for it is in principle impossible to know all the quantities that characterize the present. All sensation ("alles Wahrnehmen") is therefore a selection from a wealth of possibilities and a restriction of that which is possible in the future.

Since the statistical character of the quantum theory is so closely connected with the inaccuracy of all sensations, one might be tempted to suggest that behind the statistical world of the sensations there is hidden a "real" world in which the law of causality is valid. But in Heisenberg's view the task of physics is only to give a formal description of the relations between sensations, and such a speculation therefore appears to be sterile and meaningless.

* * *

Bohr took the next step in interpreting the quantal formalism. His discussion covers almost the same ground as Heisenberg's and his views are similar in many respects. Yet there is a significant change of perspective that indicates the direction of the further clarification. As in the development leading to matrix mechanics, no single factor has been more important for the advance of the interpretation question than the fruitful interaction between Heisenberg's and Bohr's approach to physics.

The following attempts to review the main points of Bohr's paper.[1] As is well known, his style does not readily lend his writings to a review. In Bohr's writings on epistemological matters it seems to be unusually difficult to separate the content from the style. The following exposition of some of his ideas is therefore, as far as content is

[1] "The Quantum Postulate and the Recent Development of Atomic Theory," *Nature* **121**, 580 (1928) (reprinted in *Atomic Theory and the Description of Nature.*

concerned, an approximation whose accuracy it is difficult to appraise.

Bohr's paper describes "a certain general point of view" regarding the nature of the description problem in quantum physics. This viewpoint was believed to be suited "to give an impression of the general trend of the development of the theory from its very beginning."[1] Characteristically, it was also hoped "to be helpful in order to harmonize the apparently conflicting views taken by different scientists."[2] Although not explicitly stated in the paper, the principal aim apparently was to give adequate expression to the idea that quantum physics should be considered in every respect a generalization of classical theory.

The starting point of Bohr's analysis was strikingly different from Heisenberg's. Bohr's discussion was not prefaced by comments on the meaning of the interpretation question. Instead, the issue was introduced by the remarks: "The quantum theory is characterized by the acknowledgement of a fundamental limitation in the classical physical ideas when applied to atomic phenomena. The situation thus created is of a peculiar nature, since our interpretation of the experimental material rests essentially upon the classical concepts."[3] In the analysis of the ensuing description problem, the mathematical scheme did not play the primary role, and no explicit stand was taken on a question like that of the relation between the quantal formalism and nature. Rather, the whole argument was based on a certain postulate, called the quantum postulate, which was said to express the essence of the quantum theory. This crucial postulate

[1] *Atomic Theory and The Description of Nature*, p. 52.
[2] *Ibid.*   [3] *Op. cit.*, p. 53.

was characterized in the following laconic way: "[it] attributes to any atomic process an essential discontinuity or rather individuality, completely foreign to the classical theories and symbolized by Planck's quantum of action."[1]

After these brief remarks on the character of the issue and the basis for its analysis, Bohr immediately drew a series of very far-reaching conclusions from the quantum postulate. These conclusions emerged when the postulate was contrasted with what Bohr considered the fundamental assumption underlying the usual description of physical phenomena. According to that assumption physical phenomena "may be observed without disturbing them appreciably."[2] However, the quantum postulate implies that in observations of atomic phenomena, the interaction between object and measuring apparatus cannot be made arbitrarily small or be completely compensated for. As a consequence, "an independent reality in the ordinary physical sense can neither be ascribed to the phenomena nor to the agencies of observation."[3]

Thus, according to Bohr, the locus of the quantum's physical significance is to be found in the relation between phenomenon and measuring tool. In the classical description this relation required little attention because the link between its two parts could be disregarded or controlled. Yet, when the phenomenon–instrument relation is made fundamental, the basis of the classical description seems to contain a peculiar conceptual tension, and a clash between its conflicting elements is apparently prevented only by the lucky circumstance that the crucial interaction can be made arbitrarily small.

The most important feature of Bohr's approach to the

[1] Ibid.   [2] Ibid.   [3] Op. cit., p. 54.

description problem in quantum physics would seem to be his insistence on retaining all the conceptual elements of the classical scheme, which in his usage is an idealization, and to seek a more general mode of description by exploiting the conceptual tension between these elements. In the wider conceptual framework, the elements whose conflict was suppressed in the idealization are no longer combined but are separated and mutually exclusive.

To explore the implications of the quantum-imposed "individuality" of physical processes one must identify the conceptual elements of the classical scheme or, in Bohr's language, exhibit the presuppositions for unambiguous application of the elementary physical concepts. Then one must investigate to what extent these presuppositions are compatible with the quantum postulate. In the present context, the relevant concepts are those that are connected with the distinction between system and instrument.

The possibility of isolating a physical system, *i.e.* of eliminating all external influences, is basic to the idea of a well-defined state of the system. The state concept is in turn basic to the idea of a strict connection between physical states, *i.e.* to the concept of causality. On the other hand, in order to be observed a physical system must interact with a measuring apparatus. In most cases, it is to some extent arbitrary where the separation is drawn between the objects under investigation and the experimental tools, but in any observational situation there must be some physical agency that is not included in the system and that serves to define the experimental conditions. Basic to the description of these conditions are the concepts of space and time. Correspondingly, the prototype of physical measurements is space–time coordination, a procedure where the object is repeatedly brought in contact with the reference frame consisting of a grid of rigidly connected rulers and synchronized clocks.

When these considerations are confronted by the quantum postulate one sees that due to the irreducible and undefinable interaction accompanying an observation, the concepts of state and observation are no longer fully compatible. In a situation where one can speak of a well-defined state of a physical system, it is impossible to make any observation on the system. Under such circumstances one may be able to apply the concept of causality but the concepts of space and time "lose their immediate sense."[1] On the other hand, if conditions are arranged such that contact can be established between the system and some measuring instruments, then one may use the space–time concepts yet no longer ascribe a state to the system and "there can be no question of causality in the ordinary sense of the word."[2]

The quantum postulate thus destroys the possibility of combining the two fundamental components of the classical description. Yet, although the quantum description is not a causal space–time scheme, both causality and space–time coordination are retained. These two components are now mutually exclusive or complementary to each other. When we can coordinate events in space and time, there are no causal but only statistical relationships between the events. When we can use the claim of causality, as in applying the conservation laws for momentum and energy, the concepts of space and time are not legitimate.

[1] *Ibid.* [2] *Ibid.*

The complementary character of the two sets of concepts is strikingly illustrated in the contrasting experimental evidence regarding the nature of light and the constituents of matter. One part of this evidence is accounted for in terms of space and time, another part is interpreted by means of the dynamical conservation laws. The two parts are not contradictory but are "complementary pictures of the phenomena, which only together offer a natural generalization of the classical mode of description."[1]

The subsequent sections of Bohr's paper serve to demonstrate and to illuminate the thesis that the quantum scheme is a complementary mode of description. It is shown that the concept of complementarity is contained in the simple quantum formulae, established before the algorithm had been discovered, that connect the energy and momentum of a light quantum or a material particle with the frequency and wave number of a harmonic light or matter wave. By superposition of harmonic waves a wave group of limited extent in space and time can be constructed, and the velocity of the particle can be identified with the group velocity of the associated wave field. But a wave group does not have a well-defined frequency and wave number. In fact, according to the theory of the resolving power of optical instruments, the product of the spatial extension of the wave packet and the range of wave numbers of its interfering harmonic constituents, as well as the product of its time duration and frequency range, is at least of the order of unity. When combined with the quantum formulae mentioned above this immediately leads to the indeterminacy relations which "may be regarded as a simple symbolic

[1] *Op. cit.*, p. 56.

[109]

expression for the complementary nature of the space–time description and the claim of causality."[1]

Next, Bohr discussed some imaginary experiments designed to illustrate the measurability of position and momentum in quantum theory. These experiments were also analyzed by Heisenberg. Bohr's discussion is not only an essential refinement of the previous analysis, but in important respects it places the topic in a different light.

In Bohr's terminology, space–time coordination symbolizes the idealization of observation, whereas the claim of causality represents the idealization of definition. The consistency of a complementarity theory "can be judged only by weighing the possibilities of definition and observation."[2] Heisenberg had shown "the inevitability of the quantum postulate in the estimation of the possibilities of measurement."[3] However, "a closer investigation of the possibilities of definition would still seem necessary in order to bring out the general complementary character of the description."[4]

This is a cardinal point of the discussion. The terminology of "possibilities of observation" and "possibilities of definition," introduced with minimum preparation and explanation, was to become the medium for expressing fundamental aspects of Bohr's attitude to the description problem in quantum physics. In particular, it was to be used to characterize the differences between Bohr's and Heisenberg's approach to that problem.

One of the most important issues in the measurement analysis is the question of the nature and origin of the uncertainties involved in the determination of conjugate

[1] *Op. cit.*, p. 60.   [2] *Op. cit.*, p. 55.
[3] *Op. cit.*, p. 63.   [4] *Ibid.*

variables. According to Heisenberg, these uncertainties were due to discontinuous changes, imposed by the quantum on one such variable during the measurement of the other. However, as Bohr pointed out, "a discontinuous change of energy and momentum during observation could not prevent us from ascribing accurate values to the space–time coordinates, as well as to the momentum–energy components before and after the process."[1] To clarify the issue it is necessary to consider closely the possibilities of definition.

The wave theory is very significant for this purpose. Bohr had shown that in the case of free particles the old quantum formulae, together with the superposition principle, immediately led to the uncertainty relations. This derivation strikingly exhibited the possibilities of definition. It showed that the reciprocal uncertainties are "essentially an outcome of the limited accuracy with which changes in energy and momentum can be defined, when the wave-fields used for the determination of the space–time coordinates of the particle are sufficiently small."[2]

Bohr illustrated his view on the uncertainties by a penetrating analysis of position and momentum measurements. In measuring the position of a particle by means of an optical instrument, the crucial point is that the conclusion from the spot on the photographic plate to the position of the particle rests on geometric optics. To be able to form an image one must use a convergent beam of light. It is the necessarily finite aperture of the microscope objective that prevents exact definition of the scattering direction with which the light quanta enter

[1] *Ibid.*   [2] *Ibid.*

the microscope, or definition of their momentum component parallel to the focal plane. In measurement of momentum by use of the Doppler effect, the definition of the object's position is lost because of the impossibility of defining exactly, under the given experimental conditions, the time when the recoil occurs. The duration of the scattering process may be made arbitrarily short by using radiation of sufficiently short wave length, but then the recoil becomes increasingly large. This does not affect the accuracy of the momentum determination, but it permits the knowledge of the position to be erased in the short time interval.

Similar remarks apply to situations where other means than radiation are used to determine position and momentum of a material particle. The point is that the uncertainty, or the limitation of the possibilities of definition, "equally affects the description of the agency of measurement and of the object. In fact, this uncertainty cannot be avoided in a description of the behavior of individuals with respect to a coordinate system fixed in the ordinary way by means of solid bodies and unperturbable clocks. The experimental devices—opening and closing of apertures, etc.—are seen to permit only conclusions regarding the space–time extension of the associated wave-fields."[1]

In discussing the general character of the uncertainty relations, considered in the context of the wave formalism, Bohr touched on two questions that were to become especially prominent in the subsequent discussion of the topic. One was the question of whether the uncertainties can be avoided by shifting the separation between system and measuring instrument and including in the system

[1] *Op. cit.*, p. 66.

parts of the set-up that were previously regarded as experimental tools. For example, it should be possible to keep track of the momentum transfer between object and microscope by determining the momentum of the microscope itself before and after the position measurement. However, since the uncertainty relations hold for heavy as well as for light bodies, such momentum measurements would destroy the definition of the position of the microscope and its accessories relative to the external space frame. They would thus make it impossible to conclude from the spot on the microscope's photographic plate left by the light quantum to the position of the observed particle relative to the laboratory frame.

The other question concerned the "tracing of observations back to our sensations."[1] When we perceive the measuring agency, either directly by letting it act on our eye or indirectly by letting it act on a photographic plate or a similar amplification mechanism, which we then inspect, we must again take the quantum postulate into account. On this issue Bohr remarked: "It is easily seen, however, that the resulting additional statistical element will not influence the uncertainty in the description of the object."[2]

The point of departure for Bohr's investigation of the description problem in quantum physics was "the contrast between the quantum postulate and the distinction between object and agency of measurement, inherent in our very idea of observation."[3] This contrast forces us to employ a complementary description in the quantum region. Having demonstrated that the characteristics of such a description are illustrated in the account of the

[1] *Op. cit.*, p. 67.　　　[2] *Ibid.*　　　[3] *Op. cit.*, p. 68.

behavior of free particles and radiation, Bohr proceeded to show that the quantum formalism is to be considered as a symbolic transcription of the general mechanical problem of motion, and that the wave and the matrix formulations of the interaction problem are "complementary in the same sense as the wave and particle idea in the description of the free individuals."[1]

Matrix mechanics had fulfilled the program of the correspondence principle: to formulate quantum theory as a rational generalization of the classical theories. In reviewing the matrix methods, Bohr made a significant remark about the second of the general ideas underlying these methods, the dictum of observability. The matrix formalism grew out of the approach to the interaction problem that was suggested by applying the quantum to the nuclear model of the atom. Basic to that approach were the concepts of discrete stationary states and individual transition processes. In the light of the previous discussion, it is seen that the idea of stationary states, which ascribes a set of well-defined energy values to an atom that is completely isolated from its surroundings, is incompatible with a space–time description of the electrons in the atom. The concept refers to situations where no attempt can be made to bring the electrons in contact with the external space-time frame. "The matrix theory has often been called a calculus with directly observable quantities. It must be remembered, however, that the procedure described is limited just to those problems, in which in applying the quantum postulate the space-time description may largely be disregarded, and the question of observation in the proper sense therefore placed in the background."[2]

[1] *Op. cit.*, pp. 75f.   [2] *Op. cit.*, p. 72.

The great importance of wave mechanics for the interpretation question is that this version of the quantal formalism clearly shows the possibilities of definition in systems of interacting particles. Because of the general validity of the superposition principle, conspicuous in the wave formulation of the interaction problem, there is an immediate connection between the discussion of such systems and the previously considered case of free particles. However, the geometrical space underlying the wave description of particles in interaction is not the three-dimensional space in which observations are performed, but the configuration space of dimensionality equal to the number of degrees of freedom possessed by the system. The solutions of the wave equation thus can be visualized in terms of a picture in ordinary space–time only when they can be associated with free particles. The interpretation of experimental results concerning interacting objects "ultimately depends on the abstractions of radiation in free space, and free material particles. Hence, our whole space–time view of physical phenomena, as well as the definition of energy and momentum, depends ultimately on these abstractions."[1] For example, in order to use observations to draw conclusions about the behavior of an electron in an atom the observation process must be so short that the particle can be regarded as free during the observation interval. This implies that the energy transfer in the process cannot be defined accurately. Consequently, such observations cannot yield accurate conclusions about the dynamic state of the system.

The peculiarities of the description problem in quantum physics are particularly striking in Bohr's analysis of the concept of stationary states. The title of the part of Bohr's

[1] *Op. cit.*, p. 77.

paper that dealt with it is "Reality of Stationary States," probably a reference to Schrödinger's criticism. In the pure wave theory of matter the concept is not important and is replaced by the classical idea of standing waves. In Bohr's argument, which rests on the quantum postulate, the quantal description cannot be interpreted as a classical field theory. One must remember that the standing wave system is a closed system excluded from interactions with the surroundings. Therefore according to the quantum postulate, it is not open to observation, *i.e.* not describable in terms of space and time. That it is endowed with a definite energy is "an immediate expression for the claim of causality contained in the theorem of conservation of energy."[1]

As in other quantum problems, one must note the possibilities of definition in order to clarify the paradoxes in the concept of stationary states. In the wave formulation of the algorithm the definability of energy is equivalent to the definability of frequency. A stationary state may be identified by radiation or collision reactions. One measures the energy of the reacting light quanta or material particles before and after their interaction with the atom and draws conclusions from the conservation law. To yield such conclusions, these energy measurements must be fairly accurate; the corresponding latitude in the time coordination of the reacting agencies or of the interaction process is greater than the period related to the energy difference between adjacent stationary states. Thus, applying the concept of stationary states implies a gap in the time description which is greater than the transition period.

The concept of stationary states is incompatible with

[1] *Op. cit.*, p. 80.

the concept of the history of the electron system. One can assert that an atom is in a particular stationary state only if in that situation one cannot draw conclusions about the atom's past history. In other words, when the atom is in a stationary state, it can have no memory of previous happenings. Such happenings would be inferable from the phase of the associated wave. Only a harmonic wave has a well-defined phase; a wave packet does not. Any experimental arrangement that permits us to distinguish between stationary states prevents us from obtaining information about the electron's phase. In the Stern–Gerlach experiment, such a distinction depends on the spatial separation of wave groups that have passed through an inhomogeneous magnetic field. It turns out that the condition for separation is equivalent to a complete loss of definition of the phase.

The reciprocal relation between the identifiability of stationary states and the time description of the atomic electrons is valid generally. It holds for any velocity of the probing particles. Before the wave formalism clarified the possibilities of definition, collisions between atoms and very fast particles (for which the collision time would classically be much smaller than the transition period) had caused great conceptual difficulties. The relation also holds in the limit of large quantum numbers where the quantum transition periods coincide with the classical periods of revolution. Here, too, it is impossible to connect observations of stationary states with previous observations about the space–time behavior of the atomic electrons.

Bohr discussed briefly the nature of the asymptotic coincidence of quantal and classical predictions in the domain of large quantum numbers. He emphasized that the coincidence is not brought about because the quantum postulate loses its significance in the domain of large quantum numbers. "On the contrary, the conclusions obtained from the correspondence principle with the aid of classical pictures depend just upon the assumptions that the conception of stationary states and of individual transition processes are maintained even in this limit."[1] In other words, there is no question of conceptual transmutation of the quantum scheme as we approach the classical limit. Conceptually, the two theories remain unchanged in the classical limit. They agree about predictions but they derive the predictions in different ways.

Bohr concluded that "the concepts of stationary states and individual transition processes within their proper field of application possess just as much or as little 'reality' as the very idea of individual particles. In both cases we are concerned with a demand of causality complementary to the space–time description, the adequate application of which is limited only by the restricted possibilities of definition and of observation."[2] The last section of the paper briefly summarized the state of the elementary particle problem and stressed that it was still open.

*　　*　　*

Most physicists felt that Heisenberg's and Bohr's papers of 1927–28 had solved the interpretation question, and that these papers marked the end of the crisis in physical science caused by discovery of the quantum of action. Yet many physicists and philosophers, including the creators of the wave version of the formalism, did not accept the Copenhagen interpretation. They felt that

[1] *Op. cit.*, p. 85.　　　　[2] *Op. cit.*, p. 87.

uncertainty and complementarity had accentuated rather than removed the "irrationalities" of the quantal description. Many thought those concepts incompatible with basic tenets of a rational description of nature.

The disagreement stimulated discussion on fundamental physical and philosophical problems among people with varied intellectual backgrounds and outlooks. The discussions between Bohr and Einstein[1] were central. It is difficult to find historical parallels to this remarkable debate between two leading scientists. It might in some respects be compared to the debate in the Leibniz–Clarke correspondence.[2] Both cases involve the interaction of two distinct conceptions of the epistemological nature of physics. Though these conceptions were radically different, and little contact was made between them, they nourished each other. Einstein's criticism stimulated Bohr to further develop and clarify the viewpoint of complementarity. On his side, Einstein was stimulated to give a detailed exposition of his epistemological views.

There were two issues in the Bohr–Einstein discussion. The central issue was the completeness of the quantal description. Einstein was convinced that quantum mechanics is not a complete representation of physical reality in the quantum domain. He designed many conceptual experiments to prove that the available measurement possibilities permit more accurate conclusions about the state of a physical system than do the indeterminacy

[1] See N. Bohr, "Discussion with Einstein on Epistemological Problems in Atomic Physics," *Albert Einstein, Philosopher-Scientist* (P. A. Schilpp, ed.), p. 199, (reprinted in *Atomic Physics and Human Knowledge*.

[2] *The Leibniz–Clarke Correspondence* (H. Alexander, ed.), Manchester, 1956.

relations. In his search for such experiments he uncovered several striking new features of the quantum situation. But he could not demonstrate what his "scientific instinct" led him to believe: that there are experimental arrangements that furnish an "inside view" of what happens in a quantum phenomenon. Bohr showed that each of Einstein's experiments was covered by the quantal formalism and thus could not be used as intended.

The second issue concerned the terminology. Though it caused much less general interest than the completeness issue, it seems to be no less important. It is particularly significant for studying the meeting of quantum physics and traditional philosophy. Einstein's criticism showed the need for a more rigorous formulation of the Copenhagen interpretation, and Bohr's many attempts to improve the terminology illuminate the development of his attitude to the interpretation question.

Briefly, the description problem posed by the generalized mechanics came to be to make explicit the conditions set by the formalism for applying the physical concepts unambiguously in the quantum domain. The shift from "intuitive understanding" to "unambiguous communication" is an important step in the development of the idea of a generalized description of nature.

Terminologically, the principal result of Bohr's analysis of Einstein's imaginary experiments was the concept of a quantum phenomenon.[1] Bohr came to regard it as the basic element of the quantal description. It contains the specification for how to apply the formalism in a well-defined way. The formalism yields unambiguous physical

[1] The phenomenon-terminology first appeared in Bohr's paper "The Causality Problem in Atomic Physics," *New Theories in Physics*, Paris, 1939.

statements only when applied to a quantum phenomenon. All the epistemological characteristics of the description should be expressed in terms of it.

To illustrate the meaning of a quantum phenomenon Bohr often discussed the quantum analogue of Young's interference experiment. The setup may consist of an electron gun to give the objects an initially well-defined momentum, a screen with slits, and a photographic plate to record the positions of the impinging electrons. As in optics, all parts of the interferometer are rigidly connected to a common support. With this setup we may study electron interference.

When the electron impinges on the photographic plate it triggers a complicated amplification process which results in a spot on the plate. The electron's point of impact may be identified with the location of the spot. Conditions may be arranged in such a way that only one electron at a time traverses the interferometer. Each experiment thus results in one spot somewhere on the plate. If the experiment is repeated many times, a pattern of spots emerges. This pattern is similar to the interference pattern produced in the analogous experiment with classical waves.

The role of the experimental conditions is to define or make legitimate the use of the relevant physical concepts. "These conditions, which include the account of the properties and manipulation of all measuring instruments essentially concerned, constitute in fact the only basis for the definition of the concepts by which the phenomenon is described."[1] In the above setup the optical bench defines a spatial reference frame. The role of the quantal formalism is to yield predictions about the

[1] *Op. cit.*, p. 24.

[121]

observations to be expected given under experimental conditions. These predictions may be obtained by solving the Schrödinger equation with a Hamiltonian corresponding to the experimental arrangement considered. In the above case, the formalism predicts the interference pattern or the distribution of the impact points on the plate. Even under ideal conditions it does not predict exactly where each electron is going to impinge; it only associates a definite probability of impact to each point on the plate.

The electron interference experiment illustrates the essentials of a quantum phenomenon. A quantum phenomenon involves an object or a physical system that is placed under given experimental conditions. Above it was an electron traversing a given interferometer. To specify a phenomenon it is not enough to state the initial characteristics of the object, like the momentum with which it emerges from the source. The predictions depend on the whole experimental arrangement and are only well defined if the whole arrangement is specified. To be able to predict the interference pattern we must be given the whole geometry of the optical bench. In other words, "all unambiguous interpretation of the quantum mechanical formalism involves the fixation of the external conditions, defining the initial state of the atomic system concerned and the character of the possible predictions as regards subsequent observable properties of that system. Any measurement in quantum theory can in fact only refer either to a fixation of the initial state or to the test of such predictions, and it is first the combination of measurements of both kinds which constitutes a well-defined phenomenon."[1]

[1] *Op. cit.*, p. 20.

Thus, in order to fully constitute a quantum phenomenon the experimental arrangement must contain both a device to "prepare" the initial state of the object and a "testing device" to define the nature of the predictions and to record the subsequent observations of the object. A quantum phenomenon involves a combination of several comparable measurements. For example, "any phenomenon in which we are concerned with tracing a displacement of some atomic object in space and time necessitates the establishment of several coincidences between the object and the rigidly connected bodies and movable devices which, in serving as scales and clocks respectively, define the space–time frame of reference to which the phenomenon in question is referred."[1] Similarly, any phenomenon which concerns momentum and energy exchanges requires an apparatus that measures at least two momentum and energy transfers. Conversely, an arrangement consisting of a photographic plate to measure the position of an object with known momentum "is not suited to define a phenomenon involving a test of predictions as regards the location of the object."[2]

A quantum phenomenon has two main characteristics. First, it is "indivisible." In the above case of electron interference, the physical "process" starting at the electron's emergence from the gun and ending at its impact on the plate has no definable course. It cannot be broken up into physically well-defined steps. Unlike a classical phenomenon, a quantum phenomenon is not a sequence of physical events, but a new kind of individual entity. If we are to draw conclusions about the course of a classical phenomenon, we must know both the object's position

---

[1] *Op. cit.*, p. 22.   [2] *Op. cit.*, p. 23.

and momentum. In the above setup, we could legitimately speak of a path of the electron through the interferometer if we could sufficiently control the momentum exchanged between the electron and the screen or the plate. Then we could decide for instance, whether or not the electron had, on its way from the gun to the plate, gone through a particular slit in the screen. The possibility of making this decision seems to be in conflict with the fact that the probability predictions as to where the electron will hit the plate depend on the position of all the slits.

Conclusions about the transfer of momentum would have to be based on the law of conservation of momentum. Clearly, since the parts of the setup are all rigidly connected to a common support, such conclusions cannot be drawn without changing the setup. However, if we let one of the parts be freely movable we can control its momentum separately and thus the momentum exchanged between this part of the apparatus and the object. But Heisenberg's inequality tells us that this change of the apparatus is accompanied by a partial loss of definition of the freely movable part's position relative to the other parts of the apparatus. It turns out that if the accuracy of the momentum determination is just sufficient to decide through which slit the object went, then the corresponding latitude in the position definition is just sufficient to make it impossible to distinguish between a maximum and a minimum of the interference pattern, *i.e.* to prevent us from defining a pattern of interference between contributions from several slits. It can be shown that any change of the apparatus that would classically amount to a "subdivision" of the phenomenon would prevent us from using the physical concepts in which we describe an interference phenomenon. The original phenomenon

[124]

thus would not be subdivided but erased, and a new phenomenon of a different kind would appear.

Of course, the experimental arrangements that define the elementary physical concepts are the same in quantum as in classical physics. For example, in both cases, the concept of position refers to a coordinate system of rigid rulers and the momentum concept refers to a system of freely movable test bodies. In classical physics these instruments can be used jointly to provide information about the object. In the quantum domain, however, the two types of instruments are mutually exclusive: one may use either a position instrument or a momentum instrument, but one cannot use both instruments together to study the object.

The physical reason for this incompatibility is usually ascribed to the quantum nature of the interaction between system and instrument. The finite value of the quantum constant implies that the object–instrument interaction cannot be made arbitrarily small. Further, if the apparatus is to serve its purpose, *i.e.* to legitimize the use of the physical concepts employed in the description of the quantum phenomenon, then the interaction cannot be fully controlled or compensated for. It constitutes an "integral part" of the phenomenon. For example, to give a spatial account of an atomic object, we must bring it into contact with a reference frame. This will cause an exchange of momentum between the object and the frame. Because of the quantum, the momentum transfer cannot be made negligible, and if the frame is to serve its purpose the exchange of momentum cannot be made well defined. Part of the momentum gets lost irretrievably in the frame.

It is important to realize that this loss is not due to any

imperfections of the instruments. The momentum is lost because the instrument has to yield information about the object's position: it is "logically buried" in the frame, as Bohr sometimes expressed it in discussion. Therefore, even if the object has previously had a precisely defined momentum, it is not possible to draw unambiguous conclusions about its dynamical behavior after its position has been measured. On the other hand, measurement of momentum gives the object an uncontrollable displacement and thus breaks its connection with the space frame.

In addition to its indivisibility or individuality, a quantum phenomenon has a second important characteristic: it is "closed." Loosely speaking, the closure means that the phenomenon has come to an end, that a definite, though perhaps unknown, result has been obtained. It means that the peculiar quantum interference between the various possible outcomes has ceased, or that a transition from the possible to the actual has taken place. In practice, a quantum phenomenon is closed when an amplification device like a photographic plate, Geiger counter or cloud chamber is used as a recording apparatus. Thermodynamically, the recording processes in these instruments are highly irreversible. The epistemological basis and significance of the concept of closure still seem obscure.

Bohr's efforts to center the terminology around the concept of a quantum phenomenon considerably clarified complementarity. It had previously been a somewhat broad term in quantum physics that designated the relation between, *e.g.* space–time coordination and the claim of causality, or the particle and the wave picture, the corpuscular and the ondulatory nature of atomic objects, or between elementary physical concepts like position and momentum. It gradually came to refer exclusively to the logical relationship between indivisible, closed quantum phenomena that involve the same kind of object and are brought about by different types of instruments. Used this way, complementarity stresses that the core of the quantum description problem is the distinction between system and instrument, the necessity of including the whole apparatus in the definition of a quantum phenomenon, and the incompatibility of a set of canonically conjugate physical variables.

IV

The previous chapters have tried to give a basis for assessing the relation between quantum physics and traditional philosophy. The purpose of the present chapter is to investigate some conclusions about this relation that may be drawn on that basis. As emphasized in the Introduction, the subject is still in a formative stage, and the following remarks are fragmentary and tentative.

The presentation of the topic's philosophical component in Chapter I was based on the view that Western philosophy is primarily a philosophy of nature, and that its core is the ontological mode of thought. The most remarkable features of our philosophy are the extent to which it has been dominated by the concept of being and the degree to which the foundations for the discussion of this concept have remained static. Our philosophy is not characterized by richness and flux of deep ideas, but by a stable horizon and a persistent single point of view. Despite the fact that philosophical discussion has been largely a series of attempts to free this point of view from serious difficulties, faith in the soundness of the ontological approach has remained strong.

The presentation of the topic's physical component was arranged with the purpose of supporting the main thesis of the present work: that quantum physics conflicts with the ontological form of thought. Chapter II surveyed ancient and classical Atomism. The philosophical school of Atomism originated as a response to

Parmenides' question: What is Being? In its pre-quantum stages atomic physics seemed fully compatible with ontological philosophy and was thought of as the main support of a dominant ontological doctrine, Materialism. In that period, however, the foundations of the atomic idea were very deficient. Indeed, the manifest logical contradictions which this idea seemed to involve indicated that a satisfactory atomic theory would require a new basis.

Chapter III reviewed the development of the outlines of such a new basis in quantum physics. Surprisingly, it turned out to be logically possible to create a mechanics with a built-in element of atomicity. However, this atomic mechanics was not an ordinary mechanics, but a generalized mechanics. The chief objective of the interpretation discussion was to clarify the meaning of that concept.

If epistemologically the quantum development can be described as an articulation of the correspondence idea, then it would seem that atomic physics, in entering its logical stage, broke away from its ontological roots. When seen in the perspective of the correspondence idea, quantum physics does not appear as a branch of the study of being. It is not a new chapter in the ontological tradition but rather a phase of another evolution. The source of this evolution is mathematics, not philosophy. Its trend is a search not for ultimate reality but for rigorous use of language. Quantum physics has brought the evolution into a phase where its epistemological significance is beginning to emerge. To show this is the principal aim of the following discussion.

Because of quantum physics' kinship with the mathematical tradition there are instructive parallels between the ways in which the two fields have met ontological philosophy. Ancient mathematics seemed to be entirely compatible with and even to support ontological thinking. It was thought to furnish a prototype of objects of the "intelligible" or the "really real" world. However, when the significance of the idea of conceptual generalization began to be recognized, it gradually became apparent that there is a deep conflict between the mathematical and the ontological approach.

In mathematics, the best known illustration of the idea that the scope of a conceptual framework can be extended by the logical process of generalization is the extension of the number concept to include fractions, negative, irrational and complex numbers. Such generalized numbers make it possible to solve more general problems, prove more general theorems, and express relationships between previously unconnected concepts. The idea of conceptual generalization has become one of the most typical features of the mathematical approach and has pervaded all branches of mathematics. Yet an attitude to the nature of mathematics that is in conformity with this idea has developed very slowly. The ontological character of our philosophy has surely been the main obstacle to this development.

Generalized numbers were introduced through pressure from the mathematical procedure itself more than by a conscious innovation by mathematicians. These extensions of the number concept were often at first resisted but then gradually tolerated for their undeniable usefulness. Frequently the creation of a suitable notation made it easier to accept the generalizations. Thus, it was the use of letters from the alphabet to designate a number which taught mathematicians the utility of negative quantities. Remarkably, the difficulties obstructing the appreciation of generalized concepts were widely similar in each new case. The reasons for regarding negative quantities as false or ungenuine numbers and for calling $\sqrt{2}$ an irrational concept are similar to those that led Leibniz to call $\sqrt{-1}$ an amphibian between Being and non-Being. Of course, the puzzle presented by generalized numbers concerns primarily their ontological status. If one considers a number as a collection of units in an ontological sense, one cannot accept negative quantities nor can one regard ratios of integers as genuine numbers. Still less does it seem possible to ontologically accommodate the further extensions of the number concept.

A particularly instructive example of the conflict between the mathematical and the ontological approach is presented by the development of the ideas of continuity and variability—ideas that are intimately related to the atom concept. Surprisingly, even though these ideas are part of common language, it seemed to be impossible to formulate them consistently within the framework of common language. Their association since Antiquity with paradoxes such as Zeno's indicated that although they seemed familiar, their logical basis had not been grasped.

Differential and integral calculus brought the study of the ideas of continuity and variability into a new stage. But even with an algorithm available, it proved very difficult to clarify the fundamental concepts. It took about a century to formulate the basis of the calculus. In the meantime, there were many attempts to draw far-reaching philosophical conclusions from the new conceptual situation in the calculus. Though these often stimulated philosophical debate, most were later found to be premature. The obscurity of the basis of the calculus also encouraged the view that mathematics is unable to clarify its own foundations, and that a solid basis of the calculus would have to be provided by philosophy of science.

The calculus confronted mathematicians with two new ideas, the derivative and integral. Their analysis produced conceptual problems that seem similar in many respects to those raised by the commutation relations in quantum mechanics. One could not define the derivative and the integral with ordinary arithmetic procedures. Newton had used analogies like the flow of a liquid, and Leibniz had been guided by his "principle of continuity." The ensuing terminology admittedly was not fully satisfactory from a logical point of view, but it seemed to reflect the essentials of the situation and to make the algorithm easy to use.

However, a discussion of the foundations of the new scheme began soon after the calculus was established, stimulated perhaps by the controversy between followers of Newton and Leibniz. Many logical deficiencies of the current terminology were exposed. Criticism was directed especially at the definition of the derivative. It was commonly defined as "an ultimate ratio of evanescent increments," "a prime ratio of nascent augments" or "a ratio of quantities at the instant they vanish." Evanescent increments, etc. were also called "infinitesimals," "inassignables" or "qualitative zeros." Berkeley mockingly called evanescent increments "ghosts of departed quantities." He held concepts like instantaneous velocity to be self-contradictory.

The defenders of the calculus compared the new methods to other mathematical innovations like negative or imaginary roots of equations. Although the fertility of such innovations could hardly be questioned, it was often very difficult to explain their meaning. If one tried to define them in terms of commonly accepted mathematical ideas they appeared to be contradictory. If one tried to express their intuitive meaning, the result was more figurative than rigorous. This peculiar state of affairs encouraged the view that in order to present the foundations of the calculus one had to strike a balance between logical and intuitive clarity.

It is particularly interesting that the search for a logically satisfactory terminology gradually changed direction. When mathematicians tried to avoid the objectionable picturesque description of the transition from a ratio of finite differences to a derivative, they realized that a major source of the conceptual troubles was the very physical analogies and metaphysical principles that had helped to create the algorithm. While similies like the flow of a liquid, or a dictum that nature makes no jumps had suggested an intuitive understanding of the basic concepts, it seemed impossible to formulate them sharply. Moreover, the intuitive view they suggested did not seem to point to the logically essential elements of the situation but to logically irrelevant features.

What revealed the clue to a rigorous formulation of the concepts of derivative and integral was the increasing arithmetization of mathematics. The idea of a functional relationship between two variables became fundamental. The notions of independent and dependent variables play a crucial role in Couchy's definition of the limit concept. This arithmetical definition which contains no reference to steady flow or uninterrupted approach is the logical core of the derivative and the integral. In the well-known epsilon–delta definition of a limit, the conceptual emphasis has been shifted from the intuitive domain of "tending towards" or "continually approaching" to the arithmetical domain of "pick an arbitrary number ϵ, then determine a number δ, depending on the free choice of ϵ, so that a certain inequality is fulfilled." The old difficulties of describing the process of generating a quantity have become irrelevant, since the derivative is no longer considered an "ultimate ratio."

In his treatise on the conceptual development of the calculus, Boyer[1] attempted to identify the main factors that were inimical to this development. The most manifest of these, he finds, was "the rigid insistence on the exclusion from mathematics of any idea not at the time allowing of strict logical interpretation."[2] This factor was responsible for excluding the concepts that led to the calculus from Greek mathematics. Another factor, "more subtle, and therefore serious [was] the failure, at various stages, to give to the concepts employed as concise and formal a definition as was possible at the time."[3] If the Greek mathematicians had demanded of Zeno an explicit and unambiguous specification of the conditions of his problems they might have been less inclined to ban the concept of infinity from their reasoning. Similarly, had Newton and Leibniz given more attention to developing a precise terminology, the period of indecision about the meaning of fundamental concepts might have been shortened.

However, according to Boyer, "in all probability . . . the chief obstacle in the way of the development of the calculus was a misunderstanding as to the nature of mathematics."[4] Since Antiquity mathematics has gene-

[1] Carl B. Boyer, *The History of the Calculus and its Conceptual Development*, New York, 1959.
[2] *Op. cit.*, p. 301.   [3] *Op. cit.*, p. 302.   [4] *Op. cit.*, p. 303.

rally been thought to be a branch of either empirical science or transcendental philosophy. Both views have restricted the development of mathematics. The former view has tended to let physical considerations dictate the formulation of mathematical postulates and to exclude from mathematics concepts that had no "counterpart" in nature. The latter view, which assumes a transcendental reality, has permitted the existence of idealized mathematical entities. But it too has claimed that since the postulates must conform to the assumed ontology, they can be established "categorically."

As a result of the increasing formalization of mathematics, a third view has gradually gained support. Its development is closely linked to clarification of the meaning of the limit concept. It claims that mathematics is independent equally of physics and metaphysics. No constraints can be imposed on the development of mathematics from outside. Postulating is restricted only by the requirement of mutual consistency. The legitimacy of a concept does not depend on whether the concept reflects physical reality or conforms to philosophical principles, but it depends solely on the logical consistency of the relations into which the concept enters.

The history of the mathematical ideas of continuity and variability from intuitive and qualitative origins to recognition of their generalized and arithmetical nature is a striking parallel to the development of the atomistic view of nature. Both subjects had been intimately associated with ontological philosophy since Antiquity. In both fields, peculiar paradoxes had long been attached to the fundamental concepts. The logically significant elements of these concepts began to emerge only after they had been incorporated in an algorithm. In the case of mathematics, this was accompanied by an increasing separation from metaphysics. Mathematics was gradually detached from the whole set of philosophical problems about Being and regarded as a field that requires no concrete or ideal substratum.

When compared with the course of the discussion on the foundations of the calculus, the quantum discussion appears to be still in its early stages. We seem to be still struggling to express the characteristics of the quantum situation in ontological terms. We are baffled by questions like: Which ontological status can one give an entity like an electron that appears to be an elementary particle of matter and yet is able to interfere with itself like a wave? What kind of jump is a quantum jump? Are the quantum probability waves subjective or objective, or do they perhaps possess an intermediate degree of reality? A quantum object like a photon appears indeed to be an amphibian between Being and non-Being. We seem forced to ask whether Heisenberg's relations imply an uncertainty only in the realm of Knowledge or whether the uncertainty pertains to Being itself. We are troubled by our difficulties in imagining what sort of ontological process is taking place when the wave packet is being "reduced," or when there occurs a transition from the possible to the actual. Does this transition take place in the physical realm, or is the collapse of the wave function a process in the mind of the observer?

It is tempting to compare much of the present discussion on the foundations of quantum physics with the eighteenth-century discussion on the foundations of the calculus. Many of our attempts to express the characteristics of the quantal description may be as unsatisfactory as the early attempts to express the meaning of a derivative. Phrases like "wave-particle duality," "uncontrollable interaction," "feature of wholeness," may be as preliminary as were phrases like "ultimate ratio of evanescent increments" or "ratio of qualitive zeros." Our "collapse of the wave function" may be as much a "ghost of a departed quantity" as were "quantities at the instant when they vanish." Though a terminology of this sort seems very suggestive, it may be subtly misleading. The next development presumably will not be a refinement of this usage; as in the calculus, we may have to look in a different direction for a rigorous terminology.

The parallel between the responses to generalized concepts and schemes in mathematics and to a generalized mechanics in physics extends to the attempts to resolve the conflict with ontology. In mathematics, it was realized that the creation of mathematical schemes is not bound by ontological criteria. At that stage, however, the conflict was not thought to indicate the failure of the ontological approach. Nor did it suggest that the new aspects of the axiomatic procedure might have profound epistemological significance. For mathematicians, it seemed sufficient to stress mathematics' independence from ontology. Philosophers tried to cope with generalized conceptual schemes by assigning them a realm of being separate from that of "matters of fact." Such schemes were commonly regarded as figments of the human imagination. In the world of ideas the mind can play freely. Here it can produce abstract structures that are constrained only by the requirement of consistency. The sharp distinction between abstract ideas and matters of fact typical of the Empiricist school seemed to give mathematics enough freedom and to ontologically accommodate generalized schemes. It is true that this distinction

[137]

generated its own problems, especially that of the relation between the two disjoint realms of being. But philosophers were well acquainted with problems of that type and the mathematical approach seemed to have no bearing on them, whatever their solution.

When the quantum development brought into physics problems similar to those raised by the generalization idea in mathematics, ontological stipulations began to seem as irrelevant to the description of nature as they had previously seemed to mathematics. Many physicists and philosophers responded to the difficulties by stressing that physics, like mathematics, is independent of ontology. Of course, in physics there is, in addition to the requirement of consistency, a further constraint on the mind's play with ideas. Physics is an experimental science, and thus if an abstract structure conceived by the human imagination is to be a legitimate physical theory, its predictions must fit the experimental data. But logical consistency and experimental validation of predictions are the only constraints on the creation of physical theories. The theories may be completely unvisualizable and inaccessible to intuitive understanding; they need conform to no ontological requirements. Abstract theories were commonly called models, and the models were supposed to be linked to facts or anchored to the world of experience by "rules of correspondence." A model is always provisional and may be replaced by a better one, *e.g.* one that is simpler or covers more facts.

The view described above is widely held by physicists. It appears to settle the question of physics' relation to mathematics, for it gives physics all the freedom of theory construction that is compatible with the fact that physics is an experimental science. If this neo-Empiricist version of the relation between physics and mathematics is adequate, then it would seem that fruitful problems are as unlikely to be found in the "model-rules of correspondence-data" conception as in the original division between the world of ideas and matters of fact. In that case the vital parts of the mathematical description of nature are not to be found in what was traditionally called its foundations but solely in its expanding frontiers.

The tendency to characterize the quantal description in ontological terms is conspicuous also in the early phases of the Copenhagen interpretation. As described in Chapter III, the starting point for Heisenberg's analysis of the interpretation question was his conjecture that the experiments permitted by the quantal formalism are just the same as those permitted by nature itself in the quantum domain. The Heisenberg conjecture was not construed as a hypothesis of isomorphism between the quantal formalism and the quantal world. It was given a somewhat weaker ontological meaning: unlike the classical formalism, which mirrors the classical world, the quantal formalism does not reflect the quantum domain's structure of being, but rather represents the structure of a classical experimenter's interaction with the quantal world. The main characteristic of this interaction is that the experimenter's possibilities of measurement are restricted in the quantum domain.

The alleged quantum-imposed restrictions on experimentation became the focal point of subsequent discussion. Initial attempts to understand the restrictions remained within the scheme of ontological philosophy. For example, it was argued that the restrictions originate from the fact that in the quantal world we cannot know the phenomena as they really are, because in trying to observe them we disturb them. The means of observation available to us are too crude to avoid the disturbance completely. Our relation to the quantal world is analogous to that of a giant trying to observe our world. On our scale his interaction with us is so violent that he crushes or at least changes what he tries to observe. Along similar lines it was argued that the uncertainties arise because our classical concepts do not fit the quantal world. After all, these concepts were designed to describe physical phenomena on a macroscopic scale, and so it is not surprising that they are not fully applicable to the micro-world of atoms.

Such arguments about deficiency of our means of observation or description were of course met by suggestions that under these circumstances we ought to try to improve our tools and concepts. If a god-like eye that could see directly or with better tools than ours would find no quantum uncertainties and know what really took place, the principal task for us should be to discover tools more adequate to explore the quantal world. Similarly, if the uncertainties can be blamed on our concepts, we should try to invent new and better ones. An adequate system of concepts ought not to restrict our possibilities of description; it should permit us to describe reality as it is in itself. After all, physics has once before, in the transition from Aristotelian to Newtonian mechanics, changed its elementary concepts.

Such objections in turn stimulated attempts to justify the view that the classical concepts are indispensable and that there can be created no new concepts that better express the physics of the quantal world. Although these attempts were admittedly speculative, they often tended to introduce a dogmatic element into the discussion. They sometimes seemed to contribute more to developing a "metaphysics of the quantum" than to illuminating the situation in quantum physics. Thus, they generated much scepticism about the soundness of the Copenhagen interpretation.

As outlined in the Introduction, the discussion of the meeting between quantum physics and traditional philosophy has also remained within an ontological context. The philosophical significance of quantum physics is commonly seen as a need for a freer attitude to the concept of physical reality. This has been construed as a need for a more abstract world view. Processes in the quantal world cannot be described as chains of events in space and time. The quantum objects are new types of ontological entities with an unvisualizable behavior. Unlike a classical object whose properties are mutually compatible, a quantum object has a set of incompatible properties, like particle and wave attributes, but it possesses these properties in a latent form or as potentialities. The character of the object's environment determines which potentialities are realized. Under some external conditions an electron will manifest its particle aspect, under other conditions it will behave like a wave.

The meaning of a freer attitude to the reality concept has also been seen as a need to ascribe a more active role to the subject or the observer in the process of acquiring knowledge. In exploring the quantum world we are no longer detached observers, but we mold that which we describe. Thus quantum mechanics is not a description of nature as such but it has an observer-dependent aspect. It is a description of nature as exposed to man's method of questioning. Our concepts depend on the structure and size of our sensorium, and this dependence becomes

[141]

conspicuous when we describe phenomena on the atomic scale.

Philosophically, therefore, quantum physics has seemed to have intimate contact with the ontological problems discussed by Descartes and with the epistemological problems discussed by Kant. It has seemed to offer new means to overcome or diminish some of the difficulties of philosophy. Quantum mechanics has appeared to present a new world view that is wider and richer than that suggested by an ontological interpretation of classical mechanics. Unlike the mechanical conception of nature, the world view based on quantum mechanics is neither strictly materialistic nor strictly deterministic. In throwing new light on the subject–object relation, quantum physics has added evidence against the Cartesian division between matter and mind and reintroduced Kantian ideas.

Apart from indicating that the quantum discussion is still at a relatively early stage, the parallel to the calculus discussion suggests that progress is not likely to come from attempts to sharpen the representations of the situation in terms of pictorial analogies and accustomed philosophical conceptions, but rather from discarding these analogies and conceptions and attempting instead to identify the important logical ideas that are involved in the quantum description. A more pure and rigorous terminology based on these ideas may be expected to eliminate many of the present puzzles and to bring the characteristics of the quantum description problem into focus. In particular, it presumably will give a clearer perspective for assessing quantum physics' relation to traditional philosophy.

However, closer examination reveals that the interpretation discussion has by no means remained in a phase comparable to the pre-Couchy period of its mathematical analogue. In fact, even before the quantal formalism had been found it was realized that the quantum problem cannot be illuminated in terms of pictorial or philosophical ideas, and when it became clear that the formalism was a generalized mechanics, there were increasing efforts to eliminate such ideas from the description and to pin down the logical characteristics of the quantal generalization. The phenomenon-centered terminology described in Chapter III is a result of such attempts.

Furthermore, unlike the calculus discussion, the analysis of the quantum issue from the beginning had a strong epistemological component. The correspondence argument did not merely aim at legitimizing the application of generalized conceptual schemes in physics; it was a "point of view" aiming to bring out the epistemological characteristics of a generalized description of nature. In mathematics, the epistemological significance of the generalization idea was not a central issue; in quantum physics, the epistemological significance of the correspondence argument was a key point.

From the review in Chapter III it is clear that the interpretation discussion has still not led to a complete clarification of the correspondence point of view. Both the mathematical and the epistemological aspects of the structural similarity between quantum theory and classical theory are still partly obscure. It even appears uncertain that the fundamentals of the issue have come to light yet. However, even though at present the investigation of quantum physics' relation to traditional philosophy cannot therefore be based on a full understanding

[143]

of the correspondence idea, it would seem that the efforts to find this understanding have given at least part of a background for investigating the question.

What the interpretation discussion has given so far is an outline of a new view of the philosophical aspects of physics. As to the conditions for investigating the meaning of a generalized mechanics, the present situation partly resembles that created by the attempts to understand the "formal analogy" extracted from the quantum theory of line spectra. It is quite possible that, as in the development of matrix mechanics, decisive progress will again require that the Copenhagen approach be combined with something similar to the Göttinger approach.

In the course of the interpretation discussion there was a subtle but discernible development of the interpretation concept itself. It is this development more than anything else which seems to take the discussion outside the sphere of traditional philosophical conceptions and to point towards new ideas. The development does not support the view that the central concepts of our philosophy are trivial, but it indicates that the basis on which they have been analyzed is wrong. In particular, it suggests that an epistemological view conforming to the use of generalized schemes in physics is far less trivial than the Empiricist model-conception of physical theories. The focal point of the new approach is the problem of the epistemological role of the conceptual framework. The trend of the interpretation discussion suggests that the basis of this problem is radically different from what is commonly supposed.

The meaning of the interpretation concept has been closely associated with the status ascribed to the quantum mechanical formalism. The conjectured one-to-one rela-

[144]

tion between experiments permitted by the quantal formalism and by nature made the formalism the basis for studying the measurement possibilities in the quantum domain. The formalism almost assumed the role that we usually ascribe to nature itself, *i.e.* of a teacher from whom we learn how to describe natural phenomena. The study of imaginary experiments considerably clarified the formalism's epistemological role and was the most important phase in the development of the viewpoint of correspondence.

Heisenberg had noted that the measurement possibilities are more restricted in the quantum domain than in the classical domain. He had shown that conjugate variables can be measured concurrently only with the reciprocal accuracy specified by the indeterminacy relations. Furthermore, he had argued that the quantum-imposed limitations on measurements are due to the occurrence of discontinuous processes in the quantum domain. For example, in an optical measurement of position, the object's momentum changes discontinuously at the moment when the photon is scattered by it. At that moment, therefore, the object does not have a definite momentum.

In his extension of Heisenberg's analysis, Bohr pointed out that the conditions of description in quantum physics not only "set a limit to the *extent* of the information obtainable by measurement, but they also set a limit to the *meaning* which we may attribute to such information."[1] The quantal formalism not only fixes possibilities of measurement; it also determines the "possibilities of definition," *i.e.* it specifies what can be meaningfully stated

[1] N. Bohr, *Atomic Theory and the Description of Nature*, p. 15.

[145]

in physical terms in the quantum domain. The quantum imposes limitations on the joint *definability* of conjugate variables, and these limitations cannot be explained in terms of discontinuous processes. Rather, they are rooted in the conditions for unambiguous application of physical concepts in the quantum domain.

For example, wave mechanics, which displays the possibilities of definition in a particularly transparent form, shows that for a microscope to serve its purpose, *i.e.* to determine the position of an object with given accuracy, the microscope must have a sufficient resolving power; but in the quantum domain this condition can be met only if there is a corresponding minimum latitude in the definition of the momentum transfer between the object and the light that forms the image. It is not merely that the microscope is unsuitable for determining the exchange of momentum; rather, if the microscope is to be used for its purpose then the momentum transfer must be partly undefined.

Recognizing that the formalism determines the possibilities of definition was not only an important step in purifying the analysis of imaginary experiments; it also changed the status of the interpretation concept itself. Increasingly, the core of that concept became considered as clarification of the conditions that the quantum formalism sets for unambiguous application of physical concepts. The interpretation problem became a description problem, a study of the proper use of words. The shift in the meaning of the interpretation concept from extracting an intuitive content of the quantal formalism to analyzing the conditions for "unambiguous communication" about quantum phenomena was crucially significant in developing both a more rigorous terminology and a deeper under-

[146]

standing of the epistemological role of the formalism or of the conceptual framework.

If it is the quantal formalism that determines the possibilities of definition in the quantum domain, then the formalism itself rather than intuitive analogies or philosophical conceptions is the source from which a proper terminology is to be developed. Just as an analogy like the flow of a liquid does not illuminate the logic of the limit concept, the quantum description problem is not illuminated by an analogy like that of an observer whose tools and concepts are crude compared to the delicate processes he observes. As in the calculus, the issue in quantum physics is not to obtain a pictorial or intuitive understanding but to clearly exhibit the presuppositions for using the relevant concepts rigorously. In both cases this is done by studying instructive applications of the formalism. The phenomenon-centered terminology in quantum physics as well as Couchy's definition of the limit concept grew out of such applications and aims at identifying the logically essential elements that are involved in them. Both in the calculus and in quantum physics, the description problems were interesting primarily because they were highly nontrivial.

The new insight into the significance of the conceptual framework that has come out of imaginary experimentation in quantum physics stems from the typical quantal aspects of the formalism. It is these aspects that make the dictum that the formalism determines the possibilities of definition non-trivial in quantum physics. In particular, they give clues to the question of why classical mechanics apparently could be "ontologized" while quantum mechanics cannot. Above all, it is the study of the quantal aspects of the formalism that has produced the outlines of a new view of the language-reality problem.

The most remarkable characteristic of the quantal formalism is the non-commutativity of canonically conjugate variables. This property of non-commutativity implies that both members of a pair of such variables cannot be simultaneously well defined. A quantum phenomenon, therefore, is specified only when information has been supplied as to which mechanical variables are defined, or with which latitudes the variables are given. In classical physics, of course, all mechanical variables commute, and no question arises as to the meaning of an undefined or partially defined variable.

The fact that, classically, the physical variables are always well defined is perhaps a main reason why it appears possible to ontologize or substantialize mechanics and consider nature as constituted by substantialized mechanical concepts. For example, since the space variable is always well defined, it is suggestive to regard space as an ontological entity. Similarly, the mechanical algorithm's ability to generate exact predictions from exact initial data may have suggested the possibility of ontologizing time and physical processes. Even though, mathematically, the limit process is not an ontological process, the fact that each infinitesimal step in the evolution of a mechanical phenomenon is physically well defined may have encouraged the view that such a phenomenon is a string of ontological events. In the mechanical conception of nature, space and time were thought to constitute the immutable stage on which physical processes occur. The whole of reality is spanned by the space–time stage plus the material objects that move on it. The stage may be less substantial than the matter which occupies it, but space, time and matter all exist or possess "being" in the ontological sense.

As is well known, a serious challenge to the ontological interpretation of mechanics came from the special theory of relativity. The algorithm containing the characteristic relativity constant c, which has the dimension of a velocity, was based on a pseudo-euclidean geometry. It seemed impossible to ontologically express the physical content of this algorithm. The theory of special relativity implies that size and shape of an object, or time sequence of or interval between events, have no absolute significance but depend on the state of motion of the reference frame in which they are recorded. Concepts like size, shape, time sequence and duration had been "set in granite" by ontological philosophy. Yet, according to relativity theory these concepts are not numerically well defined until the observer has specified his state of motion relative to the system.

Besides the relativistic effects, there is another, and much more elementary, feature of the mechanical description that cannot be ontologically expressed. Although this feature is well known, its epistemological significance has not been sufficiently stressed. It throws interesting light on the difficulties that the ontological viewpoint presents for the understanding of the role of the conceptual framework. Furthermore, it seems to be related to the quantum description problem, and thus a brief discussion of it may be useful.

Even though, classically, we do not have to choose which *variables* to define, we must make a choice in order to specify a mechanical problem. Mechanical predictions are conditional statements, and to be specific they require the conditions to be fixed. A mechanical problem is well defined only when the *values* of various parameters, including the initial position and velocity of the object, are specified. The description contains no directives for this specification. In the mechanical algorithm, the parameters are "free," *i.e.* they may assume any value consistent with their definition.

The arbitrariness of the mechanical parameters is as important, and perhaps more important, a feature of the mechanical description as the deterministic character of the equations of motions. We distort the essence of mechanics when we say that mechanics concerns the workings of machines, such as clocks. To emphasize the arbitrariness of the parameters specifying the machine, we might rather picture mechanics as the activity of a machine constructor. The algorithm assumes this constructor or experimenter to be omnipotent, *i.e.* able to give the parameters any value whatsoever within their range of definition. The imaginary experimental mechanical physicist can set up any mechanical problem, on any scale and with any complexity.

The logic of the mechanical description is often characterized in terms of Laplace's demon. Usually, the demon is pictured as a giant calculator who from knowledge of the state of the universe at a certain moment can calculate its state at any other time. However, in this version the simile is one-sided. The demon should rather be considered a chooser of mechanical parameters. Of course, this omnipotent experimenter should also have access to an ideal computer programmed to solve the mechanical equations of motion for any given choice of system and boundary conditions.

Had Laplace stressed the role of the chooser instead of that of the computer, subsequent philosophical discussion might have taken a different turn. In particular, the fixation of free parameters raises an interesting problem about the demarcation of the mechanical system considered by the demon. The demon would violate his role as a chooser if he were to include himself in the system. Further, if he claimed that his system included all the rest of the universe, then he could not assume that there were other mechanical physicists or choosers in that universe. Once a classical physical system and the experimental arrangement have been specified, the system's evolution is well defined; like natural numbers, each of the system's states has a well defined successor. Classically, therefore, it seems meaningless to talk about a chooser that is supposed to be a physical system and yet is not fully describable by the algorithm. In classical physics, the system, so to say, starts only at the point where all decisions have been made. Yet, the mechanical description whose structure is the basis for defining the word "mechanics," does not start only when the system has been chosen. It contains as an essential logical element the possibility of giving its free parameters any desired value. If this logical element is taken into account, a mechanical conception of nature that compares the universe to a machine, does not suggest itself.

It is commonly thought that the "bifurcation of nature,"[1] typical of post-Renaissance philosophy, was due to the contrasts between physical and psychological phenomena, and that a comprehensive mechanical world view contains no bifurcation. Such a view was believed to imply that men are automata, and the usual argument against it was that it seemed to exclude or render illusory

[1] See A. N. Whitehead, *Science and the Modern World*, New York, 1925.

many of the most characteristic aspects of our situation, such as consciousness, freedom and responsibility. Yet it seems that any attempt to ontologize the concept of arbitrariness in mechanics, *e.g.* by introducing an "entity" that can freely pick values of mechanical parameters, would lead to difficulties that are similar to and as insurmountable as those involved in the traditional bifurcation of nature. It is true that since the mechanical variables could apparently be ontologized, one could regard their potential values as having a mode of being. However, the choice among the existing possibilities could hardly be considered an ontological process. Attempts to ontologize the mechanical description seemed successful only because the significance of a very essential feature of that description was overlooked.

The ontological approach seems to have focused attention almost exclusively on the mechanical concept of a physical system, *i.e.* a system that possesses well-defined characteristics and has a well-defined time evolution. By considering even the universe as such a system, ontological philosophy made it very difficult to appreciate the significance of those logical elements of the mechanical description which, so to speak, precedes the system concept. If their presence was noticed at all, these logical elements were supposed to have been at work only once, namely when the characteristics and the initial conditions of the universe were originally decided. We are largely ignorant of these original decisions, and the aim of science is to observe the universe and retrace its development so as to discover its characteristics and initial conditions.

Anaximander's program of describing the natural history of the world has been carried far by modern science. One can now give a remarkably coherent account of the

[152]

development of matter that ranges from the "primordial fireball," through the formation of stars and planets, and the origin and evolution of living organisms, up to the temporary climax of matter's history: the emergence of man. At this last stage, matter is said to become conscious of itself; nature begins to reflect itself in man's thoughts. The impressive span and apparent scientific soundness of the world view that is based on this account tend to obscure the fact that epistemologically it is almost as primitive as the eighteenth-century mechanical philosophy.

Starting the epistemological analysis of physics at the point when all decisions that go into specifying a physical problem have already been made seems to have resulted in a distorted view of the nature of physics. In fact, exclusive emphasis on the "given," the "decided," the "irrevocable," the "actual" may have been an important supporting step in that peculiar movement from "real" to "really real" or from "reality" to "reality (loud cheers)" which is typical of ontological thinking. In particular, this emphasis has seemed to support the accustomed attitude to the relation between language and reality, which is the chief obstacle to understanding the description problem in quantum physics.

If the structure of the mechanical formalism, and not a pre-conceived ontological viewpoint, is made the source for developing a proper mechanical terminology, then the "description problem" in mechanics cannot be expressed simply as a problem of accounting for the properties and behavior of given mechanical systems. As far as the mechanical formalism is concerned, the idea of a unique system, called the universe, seems to be a foreign concept and, consequently, its meaning is obscure. The

[153]

occurrence in mechanics of free parameters, *i.e.* parameters whose values are not only undetermined by the formalism but can in principle be picked arbitrarily, makes mechanics an experimental science not merely in the sense that an observer may initially be ignorant about the characteristics of the system or of the conditions under which it is observed, but in the sense that the experimenter may himself pick the values of the parameters that specify the system and the experimental arrangement. While the equipment for experimentation, including the machines that manufacture the system and the arrangement, may be as mechanical in nature as the system and the arrangement themselves, the choice of the free parameters, if made properly, cannot be made by a purely mechanical device.[1]

In classical physics, choice of parameters and system behavior are mutually exclusive, and as long as one equates a physical system with a mechanical system it appears to be impossible to obtain a satisfactory view of the process of experimentation in classical mechanics. One seems to be forced to accept the concept of non-mechanical systems or systems without a well-defined history, but the mechanical description does not illuminate that concept. Just as mechanics takes for granted the stability of objects, it

[1] For other discussions of the significance of boundary conditions, see, for example, E. P. Wigner, "Invariance in Physical Theory," *Proc. Am. Phil. Soc.* **94**, 422 (1950); E. P. Wigner, "The Unreasonable Effectiveness of Mathematics in the Natural Sciences," *Communications on Pure and Applied Mathematics*, XIII No. 1, February, 1960; D. Hawkins, *The Language of Nature. An Essay in the Philosophy of Science*, San Francisco and London, 1964; M. Polanyi, *Personal Knowledge*, London, 1958.

assumes that the free parameters can be picked but throws little light on that assumption.

To stress the significance of mechanics' free components does not of course clarify the free will problem, but it changes its character. Traditionally, the problem is thought to be rooted in the conflict between the concept of choice and the mechanical view of nature. If the universe is a mechanical system evolving from primordial initial conditions, then each step in its evolution is algorithmically decided, and there is no room for freedom within the system. This is contrary to our experience of being able to make decisions. However, the concept of choice, in the sense of non-algorithmic decision, is not in conflict with the mechanical description; rather, it is an integral part of it.

Of course, once it is seen that classical mechanics is not *the* mechanics but only a *special case* of a mechanical description, problems connected with the bases of mechanics appear in a new light. As in other instances of generalization, conceptual difficulties or conflicts in the special case may be resolved or disappear in the more general case. What had seemed to be the heart of the description may turn out to be a type of relationship that holds only under exceptional conditions. What was entirely outside the scope of the special case may be in the center of the generalization.

In the quantum generalization of mechanics the significance of the concept of arbitrariness has become more conspicuous. To bring out some of the new aspects of this concept, it is instructive to compare classical and quantum physics as to their freedom of choice in experimentation. Both fields allow the same freedom in constructing and handling the measuring instruments. In quantum physics, however, only one member of a set of canonical variables can be well defined. This implies a lesser control of physical events. In classical physics, not only can we decide the conditions and thereby the question, but we can also start deciding which answer we want to obtain, and arrange the conditions accordingly. In quantum physics, we can choose which phenomenon we want to study, but once we have made the choice we cannot control what would classically correspond to the course of the phenomenon. We cannot predict which among the possible answers will be the outcome of our experiment. We cannot start by deciding the answer we want and then arrange the conditions accordingly.

In particular, we cannot reverse the phenomena in the sense of mechanics. The possibility of reversing a mechanical phenomenon comes from the combined definability of the canonical variables that specify the phenomenon's course. The analogy between quantum physics and thermodynamics suggested by the lack of reversibility of a quantum phenomenon has been much discussed[1] and may be profoundly significant epistemologically. The analogy is based on the idea that both the quantal and the thermodynamical description contain "an essential limitation imposed upon our control of events which is connected with the impossibility of speaking of well-defined phenomena in the ordinary mechanical sense."[2]

[1] N. Bohr, "Chemistry and the Quantum Theory of Atomic Constitution," *Journal of the Chemical Society*, February, 1932, pp. 376f; C. F. v. Weizsacker, "Der zweite Hauptsatz und der Unterschied von Vergangenheit und Zukunft," *Annalen der Physik* 36, 275, (1939); L. Rosenfeld, "Questions of Irreversibility and Ergodicity," *Rendiconti della Scuola Internazionale di Fisica*, Corso XIV, Varenna, 1960, p. 1.

[2] N. Bohr, *op. cit.*, p. 377.

In Bohr's view, the logical basis of thermodynamical irreversibility is that "the very concept of temperature stands in an exclusive relation to a detailed description of the behavior of the atoms in the bodies concerned."[1] In statistical thermodynamics we are not dealing with "a failure of the mechanical concepts in accounting for the details of the events, but with the incompatibility of such a detailed account with a definition of temperature."[2] Thus, "thermodynamical irreversibility, as exhibited in the levelling of temperatures, does not mean that a reversal of the course of events is impossible, but that the prediction of such a reversal cannot be part of any description involving a knowledge of the temperatures of the various bodies."[3] The quantum mechanical limitation has a quite different origin: "The reversibility of the classical laws of motion is formally upheld in the quantum symbolism, but the indeterminacy in the use of classical concepts defining the state of a system at a given time implies an essential irreversibility in the physical interpretation of this symbolism."[4]

Bohr's remarks on quantal and thermodynamical irreversibility illustrate his approach to the description problem in physics. Especially, they indicate that he thought this problem to be a purely conceptual one. The question is not what *is* in an ontological sense, but what can be stated unambiguously in physical terms. The apparent conflict between mechanical reversibility and thermodynamical irreversibility is to be analyzed by exhibiting the possibilities of definition for the relevant concepts. To be well defined, the concepts of temperature and entropy require experimental conditions that are not com-

[1] *Op. cit.*, p. 376. [2] *Op. cit.*, p. 377.
[3] *Op. cit.*, p. 376. [4] *Ibid.*

patible with the experimental conditions that yield data for conclusions about a detailed mechanical course of events. Bohr's remarks also indicate that this approach puts the problem of the connection between mathematics and physics in a new form. At present, the distinction between "the quantum symbolism" and "the physical interpretation of this symbolism" is not entirely clear.

Quantum predictions' lack of determinateness also has important implications in demarking a quantum system. In classical physics, we cannot include the experimenter, but apart from that we may arbitrarily decide what to include in the system under investigation and what to consider part of the measuring agency. In quantum physics, the apparatus and the results are described in physical terms, while the "quantum state" of the system is described by the "symbolic" formalism. Consequently, the partition between what belongs to and what does not belong to the system can be shifted only within the domain where the quantal and the classical description yield the same predictions. For example, in a gamma ray microscope, where light is used to connect the object with the space frame, it is a condition that the inference from the spot on the microscope's photographic plate to the position of the object be based on geometrical optics. If that condition is fulfilled, the quantum theory of the electric field gives the same predictions as optics, and the light may be thought of as either part of the apparatus or part of the system. Thus, in quantum physics the partition between system and instrument can be freely displaced with respect to intermediate auxiliary measuring agencies. "The only significant point is that in each case some ultimate measuring instruments, like the scales and clocks which determine the frame of space–time coordination—

[158]

on which, in the last resort, even the definitions of momentum and energy quantities rest—must always be described entirely on classical lines, and consequently kept outside the system subject to quantum mechanical treatment."[1]

It seems, however, that the partition problem has another aspect whose implications are not yet fully understood. This aspect is indicated in one of Einstein's imaginary experiments. Most of Einstein's attempts to demonstrate the incompleteness of the quantal description involved the idea that information about the interaction between system and apparatus could be obtained by extending the system to include parts of the measuring instrument. Further analysis then showed that such an extension would imply that the parts could not be used for the original purpose. This was also the case for the so-called Einstein box. The box contains electromagnetic radiation, and a shutter regulated by a clock opens a hole in the box at a well-defined instant to let a photon escape. The energy of the photon is determined by weighing the box before and after the escape and then utilizing the connection between gravitational mass and energy. Apparently, this experimental arrangement permits us to draw arbitrarily accurate conclusions about both the time coordination and the energy of the photon. However, Bohr pointed out that the weighing procedure destroys the synchronization between the clock regulating the shutter and the clocks defining the time frame. Weighing the box is essentially a momentum determination, and during the weighing the box's position in the gravitational

[1] N. Bohr, "The Causality Problem in Atomic Physics," *New Theories in Physics*, p. 24, Paris, 1939.

field cannot be kept well defined. According to the principle of equivalence between inertial and gravitational mass, on which of course the above energy determination rests, the rate of the shutter clock depends on where the clock is in the gravitational field. Thus, after the weighing there is no longer a well-defined connection between the time shown by the shutter clock and the laboratory time. To be able to infer the energy of the photon, we must weigh the box both before and after the photon's escape. Having performed the first weighing and thus given the box an undefined displacement relative to the laboratory frame, we must make a choice between two alternative experimental operations on the box. These alternatives will permit us to draw different conclusions about the photon now travelling in free space. If we determine the position of the box we can infer the instant of escape and since we know the photon's velocity we can predict the time when it will pass a given plane. If we re-establish the connection between the box and the external frame, the previously obtained weighing result can no longer be used for predictions since connecting the box and the external frame causes an undefined transfer of momentum to the box. On the other hand, weighing the box again gives us the photon's energy, but removes every possibility of getting a basis from which to infer the shutter clock's position and rate at the escape. The two procedures are mutually exclusive, and the resulting quantum phenomena are complementary to each other.

In the present context, the above imaginary experiments are remarkable especially because they indicate that "ultimate measuring instruments" or "classical apparatus" do not have an absolute meaning. The freedom to shift the system-instrument partition, on which the consistency of the quantal description depends, apparently extends to forcing us to accept that whether or not a device is an instrument depends not only on the way it is constructed but also on how the experimenter decides to relate it to other devices he has already chosen as instruments. A box containing various pieces of "apparatus," like a mechanical clock, a shutter mechanism controlled by the clock, and perhaps even an arrangement to record the operation of these parts, is a "classical instrument" only if it has a well-defined space–time relation to the laboratory instruments. Instead of giving it such a relation, the experimenter may choose to bring it in a well-defined momentum state relative to the laboratory. Then the box with all its accessories is expected to display the quantum behavior typical of a system in a momentum state. In particular, even though the construction of the shutter device allows us to say that the hole was open only a brief moment, the "position" of this moment on the laboratory time scale is undefined.

Apparently we do not yet fully understand the implications of the arbitrariness that seems to be present in the division between classical instrument and quantum system. This arbitrariness accentuates the problem of the collapse of the wave function and perhaps relates this problem to the more general one of choice or algorithmic undecidability in physics. It gives a further indication that even the idea of a classical world cannot be "set in granite," and it is perhaps a point from which new insight into the description problem may emerge.

In quantum physics, the concept of arbitrariness has extended its domain from values of physical variables to the variables themselves, and one consequence of this is that even the time evolution of the system is now to some

[161]

extent arbitrary. Unlike the evolution of a classical physical system, a quantum phenomenon is not an algorithmically decidable process; it does not develop in time like a machine. Since, classically, choice of parameters and system behavior are mutually exclusive, classical physics makes it impossible to regard the chooser as a physical system. A quantum system, however, has properties that in a sense are similar to those of the chooser or the experimenter. The appearance of a spot on a photographic plate is not entirely unlike the choice of a value of a free parameter. It is true that the distribution of spots is ruled by statistical laws, whereas no law rules the choice of a free parameter. Yet, both the location of the single spots and the values of the parameter are not generated by an algorithm. Like a chooser, an electron in an interferometer does not have a well-defined future; like the choice of a parameter value, the emergence of a spot on the interferometer's photographic plate has no well-defined history. Probably there is a profound relationship between this element of arbitrariness and those already present in the classical description.

Of course, the similarity between selecting a value of a physical variable and a spot's appearance on the photographic plate of an electron interferometer does not give us a physical understanding of the act of choosing. But it removes the contradiction the mechanical description put into the term "experimenter," and in view of that contradiction's dominant role in philosophical debate this alone would seem to be of great importance.

* * *

The algorithmic arbitrariness associated with the evolution of a quantum system has been the focal point for

[162]

most of the attempts to develop a proper quantal terminology and to understand the philosophical meaning of
the quantal description. A large part of this work was a
response to ontological philosophy's influence on our
thinking. Even though this influence was more clearly
recognized than in the case of the classical mechanical
description, its characteristics were still only vaguely
understood. In the course of the interpretation discussion, the irrelevance of ontological ideas became increasingly conspicuous, but their elimination has been a slow
and difficult process which may still be far from completed.

Bohr presumably was referring to the pervasive influence of ontological ideas when he stated early in the
interpretation discussion that part of the purpose of
introducing the technical term "complementarity" was
"constantly to remind us of the difficulties which arise
from the fact that all our ordinary verbal expressions
bear the stamp of our customary forms of perception,
from the point of view of which the existence of the quantum of action is an irrationality."[1] At that stage of the
discussion it apparently was thought that, as a consequence, attempts to describe the new situation in quantum
mechanics would involve ambiguity in the use of language.
In particular, in the quantum situation "even words like
'to be' and 'to know' lose their unambiguous meaning."[2]

An electron entering an interferometer does not have
a predetermined fate. No definite course can be attached
to the process that starts when the electron leaves the
source and ends when it impinges on the photographic
plate. What mode of being, if any, can be ascribed to

[1] *Atomic Theory and the Description of Nature*, p. 19.
[2] *Ibid*.

something that is partly undefinable? In the quantal description an electron has a definite charge and mass; there was a time when the actual values of these parameters were unknown; the fate of the electron in the interferometer cannot unambiguously be called unknown, for in quantum mechanics no such fate is definable.

Bohr remarked that "an interesting example of ambiguity in our use of language is provided by the phrase used to express the failure of the causal mode of description, namely, that one speaks of a free choice on the part of nature. Indeed, properly speaking, such a phrase requires the idea of an external chooser, the existence of which, however, is denied already by the use of the word nature."[1]

The question of the properties of quantum objects was a main issue in the early part of the interpretation discussion. Concepts like light quanta and matter waves had been introduced to account for the behavior of light and material particles under certain experimental conditions. These concepts suggested that the crux of the quantum issue is a revision of the object concept, and they led to the doctrine of the wave-particle duality.

Bohr pointed out that "photons" and "electron waves" had the same typical ambiguity as other pictorial descriptions of what goes on in quantum processes. "Only the classical ideas of material particles and electromagnetic waves have a field of unambiguous application, whereas the concepts of photons and electron waves have not."[2] Furthermore, he hinted at the role of these concepts: "The extreme fertility of wave pictures in accounting for

[1] *Op. cit.*, pp. 19f.
[2] N. Bohr, "Maxwell and Modern Theoretical Physics," *Nature* **128**, 691 (1931).

the behavior of electrons must not make us forget that there is no question of a complete analogy with ordinary wave propagation in material media or with non-substantial energy transmission in electromagnetic waves. Just as in the case of radiation quanta ... we have here to do with symbols helpful in the formulation of the probability laws governing the occurrence of the elementary processes which cannot be further analyzed in terms of classical physical ideas. In this sense, phrases such as 'the corpuscular nature of light' or 'the wave nature of electrons' are ambiguous, since such concepts as corpuscle and wave are only well defined within the scope of classical physics, where, of course, light and electrons are electromagnetic waves and material corpuscles respectively."[1]

That verbs such as "to be" and "to know" become ambiguous in quantum physics clearly indicated that ontological ideas were inadequate there, but gave few indications of the meaning and implications of the inadequacy. In particular, it was unclear whether the ambiguity signified that the ontological concepts had no strict application at all in quantum physics and, if that were the case, how it was to be understood. The usual explanation for the absence of complete predictability in quantum effects seemed to increase the difficulties. As outlined above, it was customary to ascribe the occurrence of quantum uncertainties to an irreducible and uncontrollable disturbance that accompanies the observation of quantum effects. This ontological terminology raised many puzzles, especially about the meaning and mode of being of un-

[1] N. Bohr, "Chemistry and the Quantum Theory of Atomic Construction," *Journal of the Chemical Society*, February, 1932, p. 370.

disturbed quantum processes. Questions of a similar type had been much discussed in philosophy, particularly in the Empiricist or Positivist School, and the difficulties they contained were well known.

The 1935 paper by Einstein, Podolsky and Rosen[1] changed the basis of the disturbance version of the quantum observational problem and contributed much to the discussion about the reality problem in quantum physics. In that paper it was pointed out that in physics it is possible to obtain data for conclusions about the value of variables that describe a system in other ways than by observing the system itself. If the system has previously interacted with another system, then the interaction may have correlated the values of the mechanical variables pertaining to the two systems, so that the values of variables describing the original system may be inferred from results of measurements performed on the other.

Einstein, Podolsky and Rosen used this property of mechanical interactions to argue that quantum mechanics is an incomplete description of physical reality. In accordance with traditional ontological ideas, they considered the following condition a sufficient criterion of reality: "If, without in any way disturbing a system we can predict with certainty ... the value of a physical quantity, then there exists an element of physical reality corresponding to this physical quantity." They then presented an example of two systems so correlated that definite conclusions about either the position or the momentum of one system could be drawn from measurements of position or momentum of the other. Con-

[1] A. Einstein, B. Podolsky and N. Rosen, "Can Quantum-Mechanical Description of Physical Reality be Considered Complete?" *Phys. Rev.* **47**, 777 (1935).

sequently there exist elements of physical reality corresponding to both these quantities. However, according to the indeterminacy relations the product of the uncertainties of a pair of conjugate variables has a minimum. Thus, the quantum mechanical description of physical reality cannot be considered complete.

From Bohr's standpoint, the reasoning of Einstein, Podolsky and Rosen could not be upheld. "In my opinion, there could be no other way to deem a logically consistent mathematical formalism as inadequate than by demonstrating the departure of its consequences from experience or by proving that its predictions did not exhaust the possibilities of observation and Einstein's argumentation could be directed to neither of these ends."[1] It was clear that Einstein, Podolsky and Rosen were not doubting the correctness of the quantal formalism's predictions; and the correspondence argument secured the "harmony" between the "possibilities of measurement" and the "possibilities of definition." Just as Landau and Peierls[2] had been wrong in contending that the physical measuring procedures, which are in principle available for field measurements, are more restricted than is assumed in the quantum electrodynamical formalism, so it would be erroneous to contend that the available measuring procedures are less restricted than is assumed in the quantum mechanical formalism. In both cases the impossibility of a discrepancy between measurability and definability is "eine unmittelbare Konsequenz der gemeinsamen kor-

[1] N. Bohr, "Discussion with Einstein on Epistemological Problems in Atomic Physics," *Atomic Physics and Human Knowledge*, p. 57.

[2] "Erweiterung des Unbestimmtheitsprinzips für die relativistische Quantentheorie," *Zeitschrift für Physik* **69**, 56 (1931).

respondenzmässigen Grundlage des . . . Formalismus und der Gesichtspunkte, von welchen die Prüfungsmöglichkeiten dieses Formalismus zu Beurteilen sind."[1]

Bohr's answer[2] to the Einstein Podolsky Rosen paper was the principal step towards the phenomenon-centered terminology. Although he did not yet introduce the concept of a quantum phenomenon as the chief component of the quantal description, his analysis of the imaginary experiments with which he illustrated the Einstein Podolsky Rosen argumentation pointed directly to the characteristics and the central position of this concept. The core of Bohr's analysis is the emphasis on the conceptual character of the quantum problem. What is at issue is the conditions that the quantal description sets for unambiguous application of the elementary physical concepts. As described in Chapter III, the essential feature of these conditions is that the experimental procedures that specify the use of canonically conjugate variables are incompatible. It is misleading to say merely that in quantum physics an object's position and momentum cannot be measured concurrently. Rather, when a system is given and a procedure is set up that legitimizes the use of the position concept in the description of the system, then no momentum-defining procedure can be used for its purpose and so the momentum concept is inapplicable.

Bohr stated that the main aim of his analysis was "to

[1] N. Bohr and L. Rosenfeld, "Zur Frage der Messbarkeit der Elektromagnetischen Feldgrössen," *Kgl. Dan. Vid. Sel. Medd.* XII, 8 (1933), p. 64.

[2] N. Bohr, "Can Quantum-Mechanical Description of Physical Reality be Considered Complete?" *Phys. Rev.* **48**, 696 (1935).

emphasize that in the quantum phenomena concerned we are not dealing with an incomplete description characterized by the arbitrary picking out of different elements of physical reality at the cost of sacrificing other such elements, but with a rational discrimination between essentially different experimental arrangements and procedures which are suited either for an unambiguous use of the idea of space location, or for the legitimate application of the conservation theorem of momentum.... Indeed we have in each experimental arrangement suited for the study of proper quantum phenomena not merely to do with an ignorance of the value of certain physical quantities, but with the impossibility of defining these quantities in an unambiguous way."[1]

A simple illustration of the problem discussed by Einstein, Podolsky and Rosen is the system of the box and the photon described above on page 159f. Another example is a system consisting of a particle and a relatively heavy screen with a slit that is large compared with the wavelength that corresponds to the free motion of the particle. The two objects interact when the particle passes through the slit. Before the interaction takes place a momentum measurement is made on both objects. The interaction correlates the momenta as well as the positions of the particle and the screen. Thus, from a repeated momentum measurement on the screen after the interaction is over one can infer the particle's momentum, whereas from a position measurement on the screen one can predict the position of the particle.

Bohr maintained that the Einstein Podolsky Rosen criterion of physical reality, when applied to problems like these, "contains an ambiguity as regards the meaning of

[1] *Op. cit.*, p. 699.

[169]

the expression 'without in any way disturbing a system.' Of course, there is . . . no question of a mechanical disturbance of the system under investigation during the last critical stage of the measuring procedure. But even at this stage there is essentially the question of *an influence on the very conditions which define the possible types of predictions regarding the future behavior of the system.* Since these conditions constitute an inherent element of the description of any phenomenon to which the term 'physical reality' can be properly attached, we see that the argumentation of [Einstein, Podolsky and Rosen] does not justify their conclusion that quantum-mechanical description is essentially incomplete."[1]

The Einstein Podolsky Rosen example brought out more clearly than previously discussed examples the difficulties that beset an ontological conception of the quantum problem. Whatever meaning one ascribes to the word "being," it seems to make no sense to say of an isolated physical system that it has no well-defined mode of being or that one may influence its mode of being by observing another system. If the quantum problem is thought of as a description problem, then the principal issue is not reality but definability. Since the relevant statements about the isolated system are inferences, they depend on premises. The premises are chosen when the experimenter decides among the possible mutually exclusive procedures for observing the auxiliary system. The "influence" on conditions that Bohr emphasizes is obviously not an ontological influence but a reference to the free choice of premises for conclusions about the isolated system.

The phenomenon terminology further improved the

[1] *Op. cit.*, p. 700.

description of the Einstein Podolsky Rosen example. As discussed in Chapter III, a quantum phenomenon is not defined unless the whole experimental arrangement is specified. In the case of the particle interacting with the screen no phenomenon is given unless the intended use of the screen is fully specified. The two ways of handling the screen after the interaction, connecting it to the space frame or letting it collide anew with a momentum test body, do not refer to the same phenomenon but are parts of the specification of two complementary phenomena.

The purpose of the phenomenon terminology was to make the description of quantum effects completely unambiguous. The ambiguities contained in previous accounts had generated much confusion, and it had become increasingly clear that a satisfactory terminology could not contain ambiguous statements, however illuminating such statements might appear. Bohr has described an example of this change of approach: "[at the Solvay meeting in 1927] an interesting discussion arose ... about how to speak of the appearance of phenomena for which only predictions of statistical character can be made. The question was whether, as to the occurrence of individual effects, we should adopt a terminology proposed by Dirac, that we were concerned with a choice on the part of 'nature,' or, as suggested by Heisenberg, we should say that we have to do with a choice on the part of the 'observer' constructing the measuring instruments and reading their recording. Any such terminology would, however, appear dubious since, on the one hand, it is hardly reasonable to endow nature with volition in the ordinary sense, while, on the other hand, it is certainly not possible for the observer to influence the events

[171]

which may appear under the conditions he has arranged. To my mind, there is no other alternative than to admit that, in this field of experience, we are dealing with individual phenomena and that our possibilities of handling the measuring instruments allow us only to make a choice between the different complementary types of phenomena we want to study."[1]

While the phenomenon terminology was undoubtedly a major advance in purifying the description of quantum effects, it does not seem to have placed the reality concept itself in a clear light. The dictum that the conceptual framework determines the possibilities of definition would seem to apply not only to concepts like position and momentum but equally well to the concept of physical reality. As in the case of other concepts, the problem is to clarify the logical basis or role of the reality concept, that is, to find which aspects of the description are referred to when the word "reality" is used. If the reality concept is fundamental, then presumably it refers to elements of the description that can be identified and interrelated.

In Bohr's program to develop an objective description of quantum effects by investigating the quantum-imposed conditions for unambiguous use of elementary physical concepts, the concept of physical reality did not play a prominent role. Although Bohr often stressed in discussions that "reality" is a word in our language and that this word is no different from other words in that we must learn to use it correctly, he did not attempt to specify its essential elements. In some respects he seemed to regard the concern about the meaning of the reality

[1] N. Bohr, "Discussion with Einstein on Epistemological Problems in Atomic Physics," *Atomic Physics and Human Knowledge*, p. 51.

concept in quantum physics as a parallel to the discussion of the ontological status of the Lorentz contraction and other relativistic effects.[1] This concern was more likely to be a source of misleading terminology than a guide to analyzing the quantum description problem.

Indivisibility and closure are the two principal characteristics of a quantum phenomenon. A quantum phenomenon is indivisible in the sense that any attempt to subdivide it is doomed to fail: rather than providing data for conclusions about a "course" of the phenomenon, such an attempt produces an entirely new phenomenon. It is closed in the sense that conditions are such as to give the phenomenon a definite, although not determined, outcome or result.

The impossibility of defining a course of a quantum phenomenon is construed as a limitation on the *physical* describability of a quantum system's evolution in time. Only those aspects of the phenomenon that are "decided", *e.g.* the mass and charge of the object, and the experimental conditions and results, can be described in physical terms. The phenomenon's "interior" is governed by parts of the algorithm which are physically inscrutable. Unlike the account of a classical physical process, the analysis of a quantum phenomenon treats instrument and system behavior in essentially different ways. The experimental setup and the characteristics of the object are described by means of ordinary physical concepts; the "behavior" of the object when the object is placed in the given experimental situation is described by means of the quantal formalism. Since the phenomenon's interior is not

[1] In this connection, cf. Einstein's remark, "Die Frage, ob die Lorentz-Verkürzung *wirklich* besteht oder nicht, ist irreführend," *Physikalische Zeitschrift* XII, 509 (1911).

representable as a sequence of well-defined physical steps, the quantum algorithm is a logical procedure that is not open to physical description. In a classical physical process each infinitesimal step is "closed," *i.e.* it is a definite physical event. The event may be unknown, but it is decided or well defined. In quantum physics the object's "behavior" is not a sequence of "closed" steps. In the quantum domain the observations are still described in ordinary physical terms but they are linked together by a symbolic or physically inscrutable algorithm.

The closure concept is still far from clear,[1] and its

[1] There is an extensive literature on the closure question or the reduction of the wave packet. See, for example, the discussion in *Observation and Interpretation* (ed. S. Körner), London, 1957; J. von Neumann, *Mathematical Foundations of Quantum Mechanics*, Princeton, 1955; G. Ludwig, *Die Grundlagen der Quantenmechanik*, Berlin, 1954; G. Ludwig, "Gelöste und ungelöste Probleme des Messprozesses in der Quantenmechanik," *Werner Heisenberg und die Physik unserer Zeit* (F. Bopp, ed.), Braunschweig, 1961; H. Everett III, "Relative State Formulation of Quantum Mechanics," *Rev. Mod. Phys.* **29**, 454 (1957); A. Komar, "Indeterminate Character of the Reduction of the Wave Packet in Quantum Theory," *Phys. Rev.* **126**, 365 (1962); L. Rosenfeld, "Questions of Irreversibility and Ergodicity," *Rendiconti della Scuola Internazionale di Fisica*, Corso XIV, Varenna, 1960, p. 1; E. Wigner, "The Problem of Measurement," *Am. J. Phys.* **31**, 6 (1963); A. Shimony, "Role of the Observer in Quantum Theory," *Am. J. Phys.* **31**, 755 (1963); H. Margenau, "Measurements and Quantum States," *Philosophy of Science* **30**, 1 and 138 (1963); H. Margenau, "Measurements in Quantum Mechanics," *Annals of Physics* **23**, 469 (1963). See also P. Jordan, "On the Process of Measurement in Quantum Mechanics," *Philosophy of Science* **16**, 269 (1949); W. Elsasser, "Quantum Mechanics, Amplifying Processes and Living Matter," *Proc. Utah Acad.* **26**, 89 (1951); L. Tisza, "The Conceptual Structure of Physics," *Rev. Mod. Phys.* **35**, 151 (1963).

obscurity is perhaps the greatest deficiency in our present understanding of the foundations of quantum physics. We should not expect that the way to clarify this concept is in refining phrases like "transition from potentiality to actuality," "actualization of a latent physical attribute," "discontinuous jump of the state vector" or "reduction of the wave packet in the mind of the observer." Instead, the concept should be freed of all picturesque illustrations and placed in a purely logical context so that its algorithmic function can be seen.

In the so-called quantum theory of measurement the principal difficulty of the closure concept is the fact that the quantal formalism does not seem to contain any logical element that can bring about a closure. Quantum mechanics may give a satisfactory account of the stability of macro physical objects but it does not seem to explain the concept of closure. The basic property of the quantal equations of motion is their linearity, and to provide closure a non-linear element is apparently necessary. It appears that "although quantum mechanics can deal properly with the relative probability of events occurring, there is no mechanism or physical theory consistent with the formalism of quantum mechanics which can account for the fact that events do in fact occur."[1]

From Bohr's view of the quantal description the expression "quantum theory of measurement" was a misnomer. In his opinion the observational problem in quantum physics was a description problem, *i.e.* it consisted solely in analyzing the conditions for unambiguous use of physical concepts in that field. For legitimizing the application of physical concepts the important thing is not the

[1] A. Komar, *op. cit.*, p. 369.

"symbolic" part of the quantal formalism but the "c-numbers" or classical parameters that occur in any well defined application of the formalism and that specify the experimental arrangement. Physical statements about a quantum object are tied to the experimental conditions in which the object is placed. For the formalism to yield specific physical statements, the relevant conditions must be given.

How or to what extent closure is obtained "in practice" is an entirely different question. In actual quantum experiments the recording device is usually a photographic emulsion, a counter, a cloud chamber or a bubble chamber. In such devices the amplification process that leads to the recording is highly complicated and irreversible. Thus, closure of a quantum phenomenon provides no practical difficulties.

Bohr maintained that for the discussion of the quantal description problem it is not relevant that "the existence of the quantum of action is ultimately responsible for the properties of the materials of which the measuring instruments are built and on which the functioning of the recording devices depends."[1] The possibility of giving meaning to the space–time concepts is taken for granted in the quantal description. For constructing a good space–time reference frame one exploits such properties of material bodies as massivity and rigidity; for constructing effective recording devices additional properties are important, such as the presence of large amounts of easily releasable potential energy. To some extent these properties can be accounted for by quantum physics, but as far as the analysis of imaginary experiments is concerned

---

[1] *Atomic Physics and Human Knowledge*, p. 51.

this is irrelevant. For that analysis it is sufficient to think of the measuring instruments as being in a logical sense black boxes with specified properties.

From the above outline it is clear that Bohr considered the closure of fundamental significance not only in quantum physics but in the whole description of nature. Classical physics did not call attention to the role of this concept because classical processes have, so to say, maximal closure. In quantum mechanics the physically describable aspects of a phenomenon are closed, but the phenomenon's physically inscrutable "interior" is not. It is this discrimination between the experimental arrangement, including the observational results, and the "symbolic" description of the object, that puts the closure concept in a focal position. However, it would seem that the concept is in need of much further analysis.

As a result of the present lack of clarity about the meaning of "sequence of closed steps" and "physically inscrutable interior of a quantum phenomenon" we are unable to state clearly the difference between classical and quantum physics and to judge the significance of the distinction between "physical" and "symbolic." This distinction may be a deep characteristic of a generalized description of nature. The requirement of maximum structural similarity between quantal and classical mechanics is perhaps equivalent to a condition which makes it possible for the classical physical concepts to be elements of a "symbolic" scheme and yet retain their usual definition. The distinction may also be a sign that the shift from "intuitive understanding" to "unambiguous communicability" has not yet been carried far enough. The situation may perhaps be described in other ways

[177]

which would put the whole question of arbitrariness in a different perspective.

The distinction between "physical" and "symbolic" is intimately connected with another characteristic aspect of the Copenhagen interpretation, the status ascribed to classical physical concepts. According to the correspondence idea, the structure of classical mechanics plays a unique role since it is the conceptual structure that is to be generalized. Further, as far as the classical concepts are concerned, "we must bear in mind that the possibility of an *unambiguous* use of these fundamental concepts solely depends upon the self-consistency of the classical theories from which they are derived."[1] Consequently, the classical concepts are not applicable without restrictions outside the scope of classical theories, and in the quantum domain "the limits imposed upon the application of these concepts are naturally determined by the extent to which we may, in our account of the phenomena, disregard the element which is foreign to classical theories and symbolized by the quantum of action."[2]

In view of these quantum-imposed restrictions, the question suggests itself as to whether it is possible to dispense with the classical concepts in the quantum domain or at least supplement them with new physical concepts that are less directly tied to the structure of classical theories and more adapted to the typical quantal parts of quantum mechanics. Bohr gave a negative answer to this question. He held that "it would be a misconception to believe that the difficulties of the atomic theory may be

[1] N. Bohr, *Atomic Theory and the Description of Nature*, p. 16.
[2] *Ibid.*

[178]

evaded by eventually replacing the concepts of classical physics by new conceptual forms."[1]

Bohr was remarkably categorical about the question at issue. "It lies in the nature of physical observation . . . that all experience must ultimately be expressed in terms of classical concepts . . . ."[2] ". . . the unambiguous interpretation of any measurement must be essentially framed in terms of the classical physical theories, and we may say that in this sense the language of Newton and Maxwell will remain the language of physicists for all time."[3] "Even when the phenomena transcend the scope of classical physical theories, the account of the experimental arrangement and the recording of observations must be given in plain language, suitably supplemented by technical physical terminology. This is a clear logical demand, since the very word "experiment" refers to a situation where we can tell others what we have done and what we have learned."[4]

It would seem that these statements cannot be justified exclusively on the basis of quantum mechanics. In particular, it appears impossible to justify the assertion that the scope of unambiguous physical communication coincides with the limits of what can be stated in ordinary classical physical terms. Bohr's remarks are based on his general attitude to the epistemological status of language and to the meaning of unambiguous conceptual communication,[5] and they should be interpreted on that background.

[1] *Ibid.*   [2] *Op. cit.*, p. 94.
[3] N. Bohr, "Maxwell and Modern Theoretical Physics," *Nature* **128**, 691 (1931) p. 692.
[4] *Atomic Physics and Human Knowledge*, p. 72.
[5] The papers in which Bohr most explicitly indicated his

To Bohr "objective" was synonymous with "unambiguous," and his thoughts on the epistemology of language were centered around the question of the conditions for objective description. In the early stages of the interpretation discussion he stated his views on these conditions in a semi-ontological manner but later he seemed to find ontological ideas unsuited for expressing his attitude. Since his remarks on the language problem were exceedingly sketchy, it is difficult to get a clear idea of his thoughts.

Bohr saw the central condition for objective description in the distinction between object and subject. This distinction springs from "the nature of our consciousness," and it is the source of "the problem of the objectivity of phenomena which has always attracted so much attention in philosophical discussion."[1] Further, "the general limits of man's capacity to create concepts . . . have their

[1] *Atomic Theory and the Description of Nature*, p. 93.

---

view of language seem to be: "The Quantum of Action and the Description of Nature," (1929) in *Atomic Theory and the Description of Nature*, p. 92; "Unity of Knowledge" (1954), included in *Atomic Physics and Human Knowledge*, p. 67; "The Unity of Human Knowledge" (1960), included in *Essays 1958–1962 on Atomic Physics and Human Knowledge*, p. 8, and especially the pamphlet "Tale ved Studenterjubilæt 1903–1928" (1928), Copenhagen, 1953. For attempts to present Bohr's views, see, for example, L. Rosenfeld, *Niels Bohr. An Essay dedicated to him on the occasion of his sixtieth birthday, October 7, 1945* (2nd ed.), Amsterdam, 1961; J. Kalckar, "Niels Bohr and His Youngest Disciples," in *Niels Bohr* (S. Rozenthal, ed.), New York, 1967, p. 227; Aa. Petersen, "The Philosophy of Niels Bohr," *Bull. Atomic Scientists*, Vol. XIX, No. 7, September 1963, p. 8. See also P. Zinkernagel, *Conditions for Description*, London, 1961.

roots in our differentiation between subject and object."[1]

Bohr characterized the objectivity problem as follows: "For describing our mental activity, we require, on one hand, an objectively given content to be placed in opposition to a perceiving subject, while, on the other hand, as is already implied in such an assertion, no sharp separation between object and subject can be maintained, since the perceiving subject also belongs to our mental content."[2] In other words, a separation is required in order to delineate an objective content, but the separation line is not fixed but movable so that what is in one case on the subject side may in another case be part of the objective content.

Bohr drew far-reaching conclusions from the movability of the object–subject partition. "From these circumstances follows not only the relative meaning of every concept, or rather of every word, the meaning depending upon our arbitrary choice of view point, but also that we must, in general, be prepared to accept the fact that a complete elucidation of one and the same object may require diverse points of view which defy a unique description."[3] When these conclusions are compared with the interpretation discussion they suggest that the quantum situation "bears a deep-going analogy to the general difficulty in the formation of human ideas, inherent in the distinction between subject and object."[4]

The analogy between the object–subject partition in psychological description and the system-instrument discrimination in physics is the basis for the general epistemological usefulness of the complementarity concept. A complementary mode of description, of which the quantal description is a prototype, is the proper logical tool to

[1] *Op. cit.*, p. 96.   [2] *Ibid.*   [3] *Ibid.*   [4] *Op. cit.*, p. 91.

characterize and interrelate experience that depends on the conditions under which it is obtained, *i.e.* on the placing of the separation line delineating the objective content. Complementary relationships were well known long before quantum mechanics in areas outside physics. What quantum theory has done is to bring up examples of complementarity which are so simple that their conceptual representation exhibits the characteristics of a complementary mode of description in a particularly transparent way.

As for the question of concept formation, the kinship between the physical instrument–system relation and the epistemological subject–object relation indicates that, just as the difficulties of giving an objective description of our states of mind are not caused by faulty concepts, neither are the difficulties of the quantum description problem. The difficulties in both cases originate not from faulty concepts but from the basic condition of objective description: that an objective content must be clearly demarcated and that it depends crucially on the placing of the demarcation line. It is the movability of the demarcation line that is the source of the richness of our situation, and the fact that the legitimacy of concepts depends on the placing of the partition line is not a sign of the concepts' inadequacy but the key to the variety and contrasts of experience.

In the early part of the interpretation discussion Bohr often used phrases like "external world," "sense experience," "forms of perception," in a way that suggested that he thought of the problem of knowledge in terms of traditional ideas. This impression is supported by his attempt to analyze the meaning of physical concepts on the basis of psychological experiences. In the first paper[1] where he "discussed in more detail the general philosophical aspects of the quantum theory,"[2] he describes "the sensation . . . which every one has experienced when attempting to orient himself in a dark room by feeling with a stick. When the stick is held loosely, it appears to the sense of touch to be an object. When, however, it is held firmly, we loose the sensation that it is a foreign body, and the impression of touch becomes immediately localized at the point where the stick is touching the body under investigation."[3] Having given this example of shifting the partition line and of the complementary character of the perception of touch, Bohr remarks: "It would scarcely be an exaggeration to maintain, purely from psychological experiences, that the concepts of space and time by their very nature acquire a meaning only because of the possibility of neglecting the interaction with the means of measurement. On the whole, the analysis of our sense impressions discloses a remarkable independence of the psychological foundations of the concepts of space and time, on the one hand, and the conceptions of energy and momentum, based upon actions of force, on the other hand."[4]

When the terminology question became central, Bohr shifted the emphasis from "the psychological foundations" of concepts to what he called their logical aspects. The principal issue now was to exhibit the logical presuppositions for unambiguous application of concepts. As for the partition between system and instrument, which remained the crucial point of the quantum description

---

[1] "The Quantum of Action and the Description of Nature" (1929), in *Atomic Theory and the Description of Nature*, p. 92.
[2] *Op. cit.*, p. 15. [3] *Op. cit.*, p. 99. [4] *Ibid.*

13+Q.P.

problem, the question was to understand its logical role as a condition for objective description.

In this development the closure concept assumed increasing importance. Closure became regarded as the key element of the notion "unambiguously communicable." Only that which is closed can be described objectively. It is the closure element that performs the logical function of delineating the objective content, of fixing the partition line, and thus of securing that the message to be communicated is unambiguous. This function is performed in any area of objective description. In physics, the experimental arrangement and the observational results are closed and thus objectively communicable. In psychology, "the circumstance that the very word "conscious" refers to experiences capable of being retained in the memory suggests a comparison between conscious experiences and physical observations."[1] The closure attached to conscious experiences is a condition for objectivity in psychological description.

In this perspective the doctrine of classical concepts' necessity and sufficiency in the objective description of quantum phenomena appears perhaps in a somewhat clearer light. It is now seen to rest on the assumption that the domain of closure in physics coincides with what can be represented by classical concepts. The statement that the classical describability of instruments and results is a "clear logical demand" then expresses that any well-defined, *i.e.* objectively communicable, experimental procedure and any well-defined observational result of such a procedure must be within the domain of closure. What we have done and what we have learned must have

[1] N. Bohr, "Unity of Knowledge" (1954), in *Atomic Physics and Human Knowledge*, p. 77.

closure. What is not closed cannot be represented in terms of physical concepts.

The most important aspect of the quantum interpretation discussion is the insight it has given into the epistemological role of the conceptual framework. Since the significance of "the possibilities of definition" came to light, the framework has increasingly become the backbone of the discussion. The attempts to develop an unambiguous terminology further emphasized the framework's peculiar epistemological primacy. Especially, they indicated that the frame determines the unambiguous use not only of physical concepts but also of philosophical concepts.

The development of the interpretation discussion suggests that the principal shortcoming of ontological philosophy is its lack of attention to the role of the framework. This has influenced the development of philosophy in two ways. Most philosophical analysis has been based on relatively primitive conceptual schemes. As far as logical structure is concerned, the problem of specifying "the ultimate furniture of the universe" is similar to the problem of making an inventory in a shop. The frame that Hume thought adequate for analyzing impressions to find the root of the idea of causality was kinematics, not dynamics. The problem of perception was usually analyzed within a frame of primitive optical ideas. As in the case of causality, the components of the optical algorithm that form logical links between image and object were usually ignored. Similarly, matter and mind have been thought of as two interacting substances or two "modes" of the same substance. In the ontological view of nature, the mind seemed a "ghost in the machine" or an "aspect of the motion of matter in its highest stage of development."

[185]

If the conditions for analyzing epistemological concepts are not essentially different from the conditions for analyzing physical concepts, then it would appear that in so far as the theory of perception is based on rudimentary optics, it contains little that is epistemologically deep. Further, classical physics did not even place the concept of matter in a clear light; it cannot be expected to give much insight into the logical functions of words like life and consciousness. Similarly, the classical description gave few hints about the role of the concept of physical reality.

In addition to having largely confined itself to conceptual schemes too primitive to reveal the logic of fundamental concepts, ontological philosophy seems to have placed the language-reality relation in a wrong perspective. Making philosophy's principal task the search for "the really real" or "reality (cheers)" suggested the view that language is in every respect something secondary. Language is a function of reality, in which reality is the independent variable and language the dependent variable. The structure of being is reflected in the structure of language. Concepts are tools to represent matters of fact. Language is a picture, a map or model of reality.

Although this view appears to be amply supported by everyday experience, it led to many difficulties. For example, the assumption that reality is like a free or independent variable seemed to preclude a deductive description of nature. To overcome this difficulty it was sometimes proposed to reverse the functional relationship between reality and language and to give concepts and categories a more independent status. For example, it was argued that the human intellect has an intrinsic structure, reflected in the structure of language, and that the mind molds the input material from the external world before this material becomes experience. In the process of acquiring knowledge, the subject is not a passive witness; rather, nature is the witness and the subject is an appointed judge deciding the questions.[1] Another simile compares the observing subject to a fisherman throwing out his net; the size of the fish he can catch depends to some extent on the structure of the net.[2]

Although our present understanding of the epistemological role of the conceptual framework is quite rudimentary, it seems clear that the various ontological formulations of the language-reality problem are misleading. The similes underlying these formulations do not reveal anything deep about the fact that we communicate by means of concepts; rather, their picturesque form makes it appear as if the problem is logically trivial. Yet, the little we have learned from mathematics and quantum physics about the significance of the algorithm suggests that the language-reality problem has to do with subtle logical aspects of the frame itself. If that is the case, both the Empiricist and the Critical school of epistemology have a faulty basis.

The epistemological primacy of the conceptual framework is not to be interpreted in an Idealist sense. Nor does it signify that ontology is relative to a linguistic

[1] See I. Kant, *Critique of Pure Reason*, Preface to Second Edition (N. Kemp Smith, trans.), London, 1958.
[2] See A. S. Eddington, *The Philosophy of Physical Science*, Cambridge, 1949. For an investigation of the connection between Kant's and Eddington's philosophy, see J. Witt-Hansen, *Exposition and Critique of the Conceptions of Eddington Concerning the Philosophy of Physical Science*, Copenhagen, 1958.

scheme. The attitude to the language-reality problem that it suggests is perhaps best expressed in a remark Bohr once made in a discussion. He was forcefully stressing the primacy of language: "Ultimately, we human beings depend on our words. We are hanging in language." When it was objected that reality is more fundamental than language and lies beneath language, Bohr answered: "We are suspended in language in such a way that we cannot say what is up and what is down."

As for the reality concept, its logical elements seem to be related to the elements of arbitrariness in physical description, *i.e.* those elements of the description that are not fixed by the scheme itself, but which must, at least at present, be specified without using an algorithm. The occurrence in the mechanical formalism of elements that are not fixed but essentially arbitrary, and the necessity of fixing these elements prior to the algorithmic generation of specific predictions seems to require conceptual reference to something "outside" the algorithm. It might be part of the logical function of the words "nature" or "experimenter" to contain such a reference. Obviously, it is the occurrence of free parameters that makes it possible to consider even deterministic mechanics an experimental science. The idea of performing an experiment, or of asking nature a question, contains the assumption that the answer is not fixed by the framework defining the question. Since the experiment is supposed to provide information, there must be more than one possibility for its outcome.

The word nature, in so far as its use is related to information not contained in the algorithm, is needed in classical theory only in connection with the specification of initial conditions and other free parameters like material

[188]

constants. The equations of motion neither erase nor generate information. They merely translate the given information into the future and into the past. But in quantum mechanics the outcome of a phenomenon gives information that was not contained in the algorithm. The quantum formalism and given boundary conditions specify only the probability of each classically describable outcome. Thus the word "nature" has a wider applicability in the quantum domain. Part of its logical function is to express the fact that on the basis of the quantal algorithm the outcome is undecidable but that a decision is, nevertheless, made.

There seems to be a profound relationship between the problems raised by quantum physics and the problems discussed in modern mathematical logic. The concept of algorithm has been the focus of attention in both fields. In mathematical logic, the refinement of this concept has revealed much about the axiomatic procedure and shown intrinsic limitations of deductive reasoning. In quantum physics, an improved understanding of the formalism's role in imaginary experimentation has led to a better understanding of the nature of physical description. In both fields, it seems to be the algorithmically undecidable elements that are of greatest epistemological interest.

Deeper insight into the epistemological significance of the undecided or free components of the algorithm is likely to come from a more rigorous formulation of the situation in quantum physics. Further, progress in relativistic quantum physics may shed new light on the role of the conceptual framework. Especially, it may illustrate the distinction between range of application and logical structure of a physical theory. This distinction is apparently intimately related to the distinction between actual and imaginary experiments and thus to the conceptual roots of physics' experimental character. At present, we do not know whether there can be a physical theory with a "categorical" basis that would fix algorithmically the values of such dimensionless numbers as the so-called fine-structure constant (the ratio between the square of the elementary electric charge and the product of the quantum of action and the velocity of light), and in which the distinction between scope and structure might be abolished. Our inability to answer such problems about the conceptual framework shows how limited is our grasp of the foundations of physics.

Danish Summary

I indledningen gives en oversigt over de vigtigste bidrag til diskussionen af forholdet mellem kvantefysikken og den filosofiske tradition. Disse bidrag, der spænder over et vidt spektrum af synspunkter, falder naturligt i fem grupper. Ifølge den første er kvantefysikken en afvigelse fra den metode, der siden den græske oldtid har været benyttet for at opnaa en rationel og objektiv naturbeskrivelse. Den anden gruppe hævder, at kvantefysikkens filosofiske aspekter fuldt ud kan beskrives indenfor rammerne af de traditionelle filosofiske skoler. Det er den tredie gruppes standpunkt, at kvantefysikken hverken bygger paa filosofiske forudsætninger eller har filosofiske konsekvenser. Den fjerde gruppe udgøres af videnskabsfilosofferne, der har set det som deres opgave at give kvantefysikken et solidt erkendelsesteoretisk grundlag. Den sidste gruppe har søgt at vise, at kvantefysikken indeholder noget væsentligt filosofisk nyt. Af særlig betydning for afhandlingens emne er Heisenbergs og Rosenfelds synspunkter. Trods mange indbyrdes forskelle samstemmer disse i den opfattelse, at kvantefysikken er i strid med visse ontologiske doktriner, som f.ex. metafysisk realisme, og at den kvantemekaniske beskrivelse ikke repræsenterer naturen som den er i sig selv, men samspillet mellem naturen og den menneskelige iagttager.

Afhandlingens these er, at kvantefysikken indebærer et langt mere radikalt brud med den traditionelle filosofi end hidtil antaget. Den kvantemekaniske beskrivelse strider ikke alene imod visse ontologiske doktriner, men imod selve den ontologiske tænkemaade. Kvantefysikken rejser ikke tvivl om, at virkelighedsbegrebet og beslægtede begreber berører dybe træk ved vor situation og derfor er relevante for filosofisk analyse, men den antyder, at det synspunkt, der hidtil er lagt til grund for diskussionen af disse begreber, er fejlagtigt, og at deres rolle i beskrivelsen af vor situation er en helt anden end antaget i den ontologiske filosofi.

I kapitel I gives en oversigt over den ontologiske filosofis hovedtræk. Der lægges især vægt paa at vise, i hvor høj grad det ontologiske synspunkt har formet vor filosofiske tradition, og hvor stabilt dette synspunkt har været gennem filosofiens historie. Filosofien er blevet træffende karakteriseret som en disciplin, hvor svarene skifter, men spørgsmaalene forbliver de samme. Selv den med mekanikkens udvikling forbundne overgang fra metafysik til erkendelsesteori bragte ingen egentlig fornyelse af den filosofiske tænkemaade.

Kapitel II omhandler de to første stadier af atomfysikkens udvikling, det spekulative og det empiriske stadium. Atomismen og den ontologiske filosofi har fælles historiske rødder, og deres udvikling har været karakteriseret af, at de grundlæggende ideer i begge tilfælde syntes at rumme dybtliggende vanskeligheder. I atomfysikken laa vanskelighederne først og fremmest i selve begrebet udelelighed. De antydede, at en logisk tilfredsstillende atomteori ikke kan være triviel, men, hvis den overhovedet er mulig, maa være dyb. Det voksende erfaringsmateriale, der efterhaanden stillede atombegrebets frugtbarhed i naturbeskrivelsen udenfor tvivl, kastede ikke meget lys over disse vanskeligheder.

[192]

I kapitel III diskuteres kvantefysikkens udvikling. Kvantefysikken er i to henseender et nyt kapitel i atomismens historie: den omhandler et nyt træk af atomicitet i naturen, virkningskvantet, og den har formaaet at indbygge dette helhedstræk i en sammenhængende og modsigelsesfri matematisk formalisme. Den har derfor muliggjort en analyse af de logiske træk af naturens atomicitet og af deres forhold til den ontologiske filosofi.

Hovedformaalet med diskussionen er at vise, at det saakaldte korrespondensargument giver et frugtbart grundlag for en saadan analyse. Korrespondensargumentet indførtes som et krav om asymptotisk overensstemmelse mellem kvanteteoriens forudsigelser og den klassiske elektronteoris resultater. Det udvikledes gennem studiet af den ejendommelige formelle analogi eller logiske strukturlighed mellem den klassiske teori og kvanteteorien, der kom for dagen i Bohrs teori for liniespektrene, til et krav om, at kvantemekanikken maa fremkomme som en matematisk generalisation af den klassiske mekanik. Dette krav blev opfyldt gennem Heisenbergs opdagelse af, at virkningskvantet kunde indbefattes i en ikkekommutativ algebra, hvori de Hamiltonske bevægelsesligninger var bevaret.

I den paafølgende undersøgelse af kvanteformalismens interpretation spillede korrespondensargumentet en mere og mere central rolle, og dets dybe erkendelsesteoretiske betydning begyndte at træde frem. Kvantemekanikkens generaliserede karakter gav anledning til vanskeligheder af samme art, som indførelsen af generaliserede begrebssystemer havde rejst i matematikken. Det blev paany klart, at disse vanskeligheder er udtryk for en konflikt mellem den ontologiske filosofi og den matematiske betragtningsmaade. Ligesom i matematikken, ledte dis-

[193]

kussionen af vanskelighederne i kvantemekanikken til et nyt syn paa fysikkens natur.

Det afgørende skridt i diskussionen af kvantefysikkens grundlag er overgangen fra at betragte interpretations-problemet som et spørgsmaal om at opnaa en størst mulig "anskuelig forstaaelse" af kvanteformalismens fysiske indhold til at betragte problemet udelukkende som et spørgsmaal om at klarlægge betingelserne for utvetydig meddelelse af fysiske erfaringer. Denne overgang ledte til bevidste bestræbelser paa at komme bort fra den onto-logiske betragtningsmaade. Et af dens vigtigste resultater er den Bohrske fænomen-terminologi, der søger at udelukke enhver ontologisk fortolkning af beskrivelses-problemet i kvantefysikken.

I kapitel IV diskuteres det erkendelsesteoretiske syns-punkt, som synes at være indeholdt i korrespondens-argumentet, og hvis omrids kom for dagen i den seneste fase af interpretations-diskussionen. Dette syns-punkts kerne er en ny indstilling til begrebsrammens betydning i beskrivelsen af vor situation og derfor til forholdet mellem sprog og virkelighed. Undersøgelsen af tanke-experimenter viste, at begrebsrammen har en ejendommelig primær status i fysisk og filosofisk analyse. Rammen spiller en lignende fundamental rolle her som i matematikken. Vor nuværende forstaaelse af dens funktion er imidlertid yderst begrænset og altfor over-fladisk til at sætte os i stand til at formulere en teori om sprogets filosofiske status.

Ligesom matematiske og fysiske problemer synes filosofiske problemer at dreje sig om begrebsrammen. Virkeligheds-problemet drejer sig ikke om at identificere "det egentligt værende," men om at identificere de træk i beskrivelsen, som giver ordet virkelighed en logisk

[194]

funktion. Paa baggrund af fysikkens og filosofiens udvikling kan det ikke forventes, at disse træk kan fastlægges alene gennem analyse af dagligsproget. Det er værd at understrege, at hverken dagligsproget eller den klassiske fysik gav tydelige vink om, at naturens stabilitet er intimt forbundet med ikke-kommuterbarheden af mekaniske variable.

Kvantefysikken antyder, at anvendelsen af virkelighedsbegrebet staar i nøje forbindelse med, at den fysiske beskrivelse indeholder elementer, som ikke er fastlagt af algoritmen, men som ikke desto mindre maa fastlægges, for at algoritmen kan producere entydige forudsigelser. Forekomsten af principielt arbitrære elementer i den klassiske mekanik umuliggør en mekanisk naturopfattelse. Bevægelsesligningernes deterministiske karakter udelukker, at man kan betragte experimentatoren eller vælgeren af begyndelsesbetingelser og af vædier for de frie parametre som et fysisk system. I kvantemekanikken, hvor ikke alene randbetingelserne maa fastlægges ikke-algoritmisk, men hvor selv systemets udvikling i tiden ikke er fuldt determineret, forsvinder denne vanskelighed. De nye arbitrære elementer i kvantefysikken har stærkt fremhævet den erkendelsesteoretiske betydning af ikke-algoritmisk specifikation i naturbeskrivelsen. De antyder en dyb forbindelse mellem beskrivelsesproblemet i fysikken og problemer om grænserne for algoritmisk deduktion i den matematiske logik.

INDEX

Alexander, H., 119

Ambiguity in use of language, 163f, 171

Anaximander, program of, 40f, 57, 152f

Anaximenes, 40, 63

Arbitrariness, in classical mechanics, 150ff, 188; in quantum mechanics, 155ff, 189

Aristotle, 44f, 49, 58, 60f, 66f, 140

Atomic, concept, 63–66, 69, 129; models, 69–71; problem, 63, 65–73

Atomism, ancient, 63–66, 128; and classical physics, 67–72; empirical stage of, 68, 71; logical stage of, 73; school of, 42

Bailey, C., 63

Being, concept of, 39, 41–44, 128, 163f, 169f, 188

Bergmann, G., 17

Berkeley, G., 53–55, 132

Bifurcation of nature, 151f

Boas, M., 67

Bohr, N., 1, 29, 32, 74, 76, 81, 88, 91–94, 104ff, 145, 156, 163–65, 178, 188; discussion with Einstein, 119–27, 159f, 167–71; postulates, 77f; view of complementarity,

2–6; view of classical concepts, 178ff; view of irreversibility, 156f; work on interpretation problem, 104–118

Bopp, F., 174

Born, M., 31, 75, 84, 88f, 92

Boyer, C. B., 134

Broglie, L. de, 90

Burnet, J., 63

Calculus, basis of, 131–37; and quantum discussion, 136f, 142f

Cassirer, E., philosophical views of, 15f

Causality, concept of, 107f, 185; doctrine of, 103, 126

Cherniss, H., 40, 63

Classical concepts, 24–26, 105, 107, 121, 125, 140ff, 173ff, 178ff

Classical mechanics, and ontology, 147–53; description problem in, 153; free parameters in, 149–55

Closure, 126, 174ff, 184f

Collapse of wave function, 136f, 161

Completeness problem, 119f, 166ff

Complementarity, concept of, 25, 29, 32, 108ff, 163, 181f;

[197]